SPRINGBOARD
WOMENS DEVELOPMENT WORKBOOK

developed and written by
Liz Willis and Jenny Daisley

illustrated by
Viv Quillin

HAWTHORN PRESS

Springboard © 1990 Liz Willis and Jenny Daisley
Published by Hawthorn Press, Hawthorn House, 1 Lansdown Lane, Lansdown, Stroud GL5 1BJ, UK

All illustrations © 1990 Viv Quillin

Copyright All rights reserved. No part of this publication may be reproduced, stored in a retrieval system, or transmitted, in any form or by any means, electronic, mechanical, photocopying, recording, or otherwise without the prior permission of the copyright holders. Material not for resale.

Designed and produced by Mary Wright, Zebra, Cheltenham

First edition, 1990
First reprint, 1991
Second edition 1992
Reprinted 1993
Reprinted 1994
Third edition 1995
Reprinted 1996
Fourth edition 1998
Printed by Redwood Books, Trowbridge, Wilts.

Printed on environmentally friendly, chlorine free paper.

Acknowledgements
Natasha Josefowitz for her kind permission to use her verse *Support Systems* from her book *Is this where I was going?* published by Columbus Books 1986

Sheldon Press for their kind permission to quote from part of Allan Pease's book *Body Language* 1981

The Training Agency for their permission to use Valerie Hammond and Dr Margaret Ryan's material in *Power and Influence in Organisations*.

By the same authors
Developing Women through Training 1997 The Springboard Consultancy
The Assertive Trainer 1994 McGraw Hill
Women Singled Out 1995 The Springboard Consultancy

British Library Cataloguing in Publication Data

Willis, Liz
    Springboard : women's development workbook.
    1. Great Britain. Women personnel. Working life
    I. Title II. Daisley, Jenny
    305.430941

ISBN 1 - 869890 - 98 - 1

CONTENTS

Think Michael Crawford/Mary Whitehouse. Be grateful you are
criticised - it shows you are getting noticed. And
its not my problem its bother someone else.
Usually its family who are envy thes, had it done to them;
repeat it everywhere; the aggressive attack those who
appear confident. Why do sick teachers ridicule children.
Cos they cant cope with adults.

GETTING IN TOUCH

You can work through this book on your own. However it is also designed to be used as part of the Springboard programme, which will give you the support of other people and short workshops to help you get the best out of this book. Get in touch with us and we'll send you the list of licensed Springboard trainers who can tell you what is happening in your area.

There is also a national Springboard Newsletter – 'NewsSplash' – which provides information and networking links for anyone interested or involved in Springboard, whether you are an individual, an employer or representing an organisation. Contact us for details of 'NewsSplash'.

Many Springboard programmes are run inside organisations. Only trainers trained by us are licensed to run Springboard programmes. Contact us for further details about how to implement a Springboard programme in-house, or about how to become a licensed trainer.

To get in touch, send this form or write to:

Liz Willis and Jenny Daisley
The Springboard Consultancy
P O Box 69, STROUD
Glos. GL5 5EE, UK

Tel: 01453 878540   Fax: 01453 872363
E-mail: springboard@compuserve.com

We look forward to hearing from you. Tick the box(es) which apply to you:

❏ I am interested in attending a Springboard programme. Please send me the list of local licensed trainers.

❏ I would like information on becoming a freelance licensed trainer.

❏ I would like information on licensing in-house trainers.

❏ I would like further information about how to implement a Springboard programme within my organisation.

❏ I would like details of 'NewsSplash'.

Name _____ Date _____

Job Title (if applicable) _____

Organisation (if applicable) _____

Address _____

_____

_____ Postcode _____

Daytime Tel. No._____ Evening Tel. No._____

BIOGRAPHICAL DETAILS OF THE AUTHORS

Liz Willis and Jenny Daisley are well known as two of the UK's leading women's development consultants, with, between them, 40 years of experience in this field. In addition to their training and consultancy work, they are also well known as writers on women's development.

Both highly respected as consultants in their own right, they collaborated in designing and developing the 3 month Springboard Women's Development Programme which first won the 1989 Lady Platt Award for the most innovative Equal Opportunities training, and more recently has won the prestigious government awarded 1993 National Training Award. This workbook is an essential ingredient of the Springboard programme.

Liz and Jenny work both nationally and internationally with clients in the private, public and voluntary sectors, as well as with women's groups. They are known for their positive and practical approach and work at all levels in organisations, creating overall development strategies as well as designing and delivering a variety of training and development programmes from in-depth residential courses with small groups, to one day workshops with hundreds.

Since the first publication of this Workbook, Liz and Jenny have delivered an extensive programme of training and licensing other trainers to use the Springboard programme and Workbook. This has resulted in an international network of over 330 Springboard trainers delivering Springboard programmes in the UK, Denmark, Australia, New Zealand, France, Ghana, South Africa, Spain, India, Finland and the Republic of Ireland, with special editions of the Workbook and further interest from women in Eastern Europe, South America and Pakistan.

Both Liz and Jenny run their own businesses, having started their careers at the bottom of organisations and worked their way up. They have personally experienced many of the hurdles encountered by women, both at work and in their personal lives. In her counselling practice, Jenny works in-depth with women, enabling them to understand the past, heal the present and take new action steps for the future.

Liz and Jenny have also written 'Developing Women Through Training', 'Women Singled Out' and 'The Assertive Trainer' and are currently researching a companion volume to 'Springboard' also to be published by Hawthorn Press.

THANKS

When the first edition of Springboard was published it was a new and unprecedented idea and we were curious about how it would be received. Seven years later, 100,000 copies have been sold, there are special editions in other countries and it is available in braille and on tape. This achievement is due entirely to the enthusiasm and commitment of many people. We've been delighted with the overwhelmingly positive reaction to the book and are also grateful for the constructive criticisms and helpful suggestions we've received. In particular we want to thank:

The network of licensed Springboard trainers. Seven years ago there were just 2 of us – now there are over 330 and many of the changes in this new edition have come from helpful conversations with other Springboard trainers.

Sandra Benjamin, Mary Blance, Paulette Bushay, Rosalind Campbell, Gail Cookson, Sheila Hesketh, Jacqueline Hughes, Pippa Isbell, Mary Nelson, Smita Patel, Rosemary Raddon, Elizabeth Standen, Barbara Stephens, Sue Stoessl, Pauline Townsend, Marion Way, and **Vikki Worthington** who wrote up their life stories. These stories and quotes bring to life the issues raised in the book. We admire the generosity of these women who are prepared to be visible so that others can learn from their experiences.

Anne Watts OBE, Equal Opportunities Director at Midland Bank, for all her support, from the beginnings of the idea, through its development and for writing the Foreword.

Mary Wright for her design and layout, and **Viv Quillin** for her cartoons, sense of humour and encouragement. Special thanks to all our Springboard office colleagues especially **Celia Morrison-Smith** for her cheerful and practical support to us and all in the Springboard network.

All the people at the **BBC** who were involved in their Women's Development Programme, the predecessor to Springboard, in particular **Jacqui Kasket** now a freelance consultant and **Bob Nelson** Head of Corporate Management Development.

Valerie Hammond Chief Executive Officer, Roffey Park Management Institute, **Eleanor Macdonald** of EM Courses, **Jean Buswell** of GWETI, and **Gail Cookson** for their feedback and help with the first edition.

Martin Large and **Anne Harris** of Hawthorn Press who believed in the book enough to publish it, and who have been extraordinarily patient, understanding and supportive as it has gone through the various changes into this new edition.

Tens of thousands of women in 12 different countries have now completed Springboard programmes, so we offer you the opportunity to benefit from their ideas and experiences as you work through it for yourself.

Liz Willis and Jenny Daisley — 15 January 1998

FOREWORD

Rarely, if ever, do I stop to read the foreword of a book before I plunge into its pages. But I hope you will spare a few moments in which I may give you an insight into the reasons for this book's arrival and its importance for women's lives.

Having worked in the field of equal opportunities it is very easy for me to see the enormous potential women have to offer both the organisations who employ them, and the communities in which they live. You will know, on reflection, of the potential which is inside you. This Workbook offers you the opportunity to take those first steps down the road to releasing this latent talent.

The fact that in many cases this potential has still to be unlocked may well be the fault of the 'system'; discriminatory attitudes of those who hold the positions of power, stereotypes of women and their capabilities, and more, but it also has much to do with our own perception of ourselves and the very limiting effects this can have on our lives. We have only to believe that we probably cannot do something, for comments such as 'That might be difficult for you' to stick.

So in looking at enabling women to reach beyond their current restricted horizons I was looking to find something open to large numbers of women; not simply those in management, but at all levels of the organisation.

Working in this area for a number of years, I knew that nothing was readily available, until one day I heard of the innovative work being done at the BBC. This was a very exciting development indeed.

This material has been developed and written by Liz Willis and Jenny Daisley who have vast experience of running women's training courses. They have been working together to launch this expansive new package which covers as many as 100 women at each stage – now this was real change! At the same time, every individual woman opening Springboard can work on her own.

Springboard encourages women all over the country to form their own networks with each other, building their confidence to such an extent that they can see how to change their own lives for the better.

This was an entirely new concept. When I met the women on their final Springboard workshop, they had literally jumped out of their shells; ready and equipped to face their adventurous new world.

If you are ready and willing to face the challenge, I can thoroughly commend this Workbook to you.

Anne Watts OBE
Equal Opportunities Director
Midland Bank

ACTION POINTS

GETTING STARTED

There are four kinds of people in the world:
People who watch things happen,
People to whom things happen,
People who don't know what is happening,
And people who make things happen.

Anon

Objective: To get you going

This section is important because:

— channelling your energy enables you to get the best out of yourself
— understanding this Workbook will help you get the most out of it
— you are faced with a golden opportunity

Contents:

— our approach
— understanding this Workbook
— getting yourself organised
— dealing with change
— your objectives
— the luck challenge
— summary and action
— profile of Sheila Hesketh

Getting started

You are being faced with a golden opportunity. Whether you are tackling this book on your own or with other people, you have already taken the first, and often most difficult step by opening this book and starting! So – congratulations! You have now either created, or grabbed, this opportunity.

This is your opportunity to give yourself a good dusting-down, to don a really positive attitude, and to get out there, challenging life!

This book is all about what you can do to help yourself. It is not about what your family should do for you, what the government, your partner, your manager, or your organisation should do for you.

It's about you accepting the responsibility for yourself, realising that no one hands you life on a plate, making the most of everything you've done so far, and looking the world in the eye, believing 'I can do this'.

It is also a very unusual opportunity. Most of us don't set aside regular chunks of time to think about ourselves and make positive changes in our lives. You may have decided to do this for yourself, or you may have been encouraged and subsidised by your employer to do so; either way, give yourself a real chance and **make the most of it!**

More than just a Workbook, Springboard is a complete development programme, which you can work through superficially or in as much depth as you want. Also it can be done in lots of different ways such as:
— by yourself
— with two or three friends
— with Springboard Workshops
— in support or networking groups.

In more detail, it:

— is about making changes

— is about you developing yourself as a whole person, not only the person you are at home or at work

— requires you to be self-motivated and committed

— requires energy and enthusiasm

— can be done in a superficial manner, very deeply, and every other way in between!

— is your responsibility

— isn't going to tell you what to do with your life

— isn't a career directory

— doesn't contain any magic answers!

— results in practical action.

Our approach

This book has been developed and written for all women currently in or thinking about employment who are not in management grades. This covers most working women! So this book is for you, whether you're:

— considering a return to work

— starting out on your career

— approaching retirement

— in a comfortable rut

— coping with redundancy

— thinking of setting up your own business

— feeling stuck

— just promoted

— working part-time or full-time

— working freelance

— in academic life and needing to reassess your goals

— in management, and wanting to review and replan

— or whatever!

The content and process of the book is very broad, to encompass women of all ages, in all stages of their lives, of all races, all levels of ability and disability and with all levels of qualifications. The approach is also broad enough to take in women with and without children, women living with partners, with elderly relatives, or women living on their own.

We have deliberately avoided using the words 'husband' 'boyfriend' 'lesbian lover' or 'live-in-lover' and refer to 'partner' throughout as the close permanent relationship in your life, if you have one. If you're thinking of setting up your own business, of course you may also have a business partner!

We have also used the word 'work' throughout to mean wherever and however you work. This covers paid and voluntary work, job sharing and working from home. If you are not employed at the moment, you can relate the references to work to a previous organisation you have worked for, to a club or society in which you are involved, or to an organisation that you are aiming to work for.

When we refer to your 'workplace', we mean your office, school, university, hospital, depot, bank, studio, factory, shop, home, or whatever, so you need to interpret this as you go along! When we refer to your 'boss' you may need to interpret that too if you are freelance or in education.

The approach is based on our own fundamental beliefs about women's development. These are:

— that you are capable of developing yourself more fully, no matter what your circumstances are

— that you have to want to do it

— that you are capable of taking more control over your life

— that developing your whole self develops your career

— that women have not had opportunities in a world that has been structured and controlled by men

— that it is the small, practical steps that work

— that the answers lie in the practical experiences of women, both at work and at home

— that women develop, achieve and work in a way which is just as effective as men's but which involves a different process

— that development is a difficult process — that's why you have to want to do it

— that you can do it – if you want to

We also believe that development, although always difficult and often painful, is enormous fun, and leads to greater fulfilment and happiness; so we hope that it will be enjoyable for you, as well as challenging!

There is no exam at the end, no tests, no marks, no essays to be written, no assessments, and no Springboard diplomas to be worked for. You set your own targets and it's up to you to achieve them. After all – it's your life!

Understanding this Workbook

This is a self-development programme condensed into a Workbook of 15 sections. Most sections have an introductory page and a closing page. Each section has a different balance of content depending on the subject tackled. It is vital that you go through the book in the order it is written. The only exception to this is Section 10 on stress. If nerves or stress are a major issue for you, go to Section 10 earlier and use the exercises as you go through the rest of the book.

The speed at which you go through the Workbook is up to you. If you're working through it in conjunction with workshops or group meetings, these will determine your deadlines. When organisations use it with workshops, it becomes a three month programme and works well with individuals spending about three hours a week of their own time on it.

If you're working on your own or with a group of friends or colleagues, we suggest that you do the same – set aside a total of three hours a week over a period of three months, and stick to it! Within those deadlines, it's up to you to decide how much time you spend on each section, and whether you tackle it in one go or take several smaller bites at it.

This is your Workbook. Please do scribble all over it, draw pictures in it, or whatever will help you make it your own, and aid your learning. You are not asked to show it to anyone else if you don't want to. It is your private Workbook of your own development, and although it is designed to be worked through as a three month programme you can go on using it afterwards, as you re-do exercises or think of things to alter or add.

In Section 14, you will find **Your Personal Resource Bank**. This is a bank of useful data that you will build up about yourself as you go through the book and which can be used over and over again, when, for example, you are:

— thinking about going back to work

— applying for a job

— writing your CV

— changing the way you work

— making a decision

— facing a difficult situation

— resetting your goals

— assessing your own progress

It is entirely up to you how you use this resource bank. There are also other points in the book where you are asked to put in information and ideas.

As this is your own self-development Workbook, and will probably include personal stuff about yourself, you may want to keep it in a safe place.

Content

The subjects embraced by this Workbook are all common sense. You may have tackled some, or even many of them, before, or you may have knowledge and experience of them already as a means of helping or teaching someone else. For example, you may have read a book about assertiveness, been on a career-planning workshop, heard about image-building, or helped someone else set their goals. In which case, use your previously gained experience and knowledge when you get to the appropriate section.

However, you will not have tackled all these subjects over such a concentrated and sustained amount of time, or worked through these exercises, or done it in this order, so do not be tempted to skip a section, but work through it in context.

The content breaks into eight ingredients:

— input
— exercises
— activities
— questionnaires
— examples
— profiles
— action plans
— 'me time'

1 Input
Input is kept to a minimum, as the emphasis is on the work that you do yourself. We have given you enough to explain the context and get you started. If you want more input and information, there is 'Further Optional Reading' and the appendices to refer to.

2 Exercises

The exercises are the main ingredient in this Workbook. It is entirely up to you how long you take to do them. Some of them can take days to think about, in which case you may want to have a first go at them, and then come back to them later. Others ask you for quick reactions and can be done in a matter of minutes.

Exercises are always enclosed by a tinted border and when you are being asked to write something down, it includes a space. They mostly do not come to any set conclusions, so it's sometimes up to you to decide for yourself what you get out of them. There is no 'right' or 'wrong' answer – whatever is right for you.

3 Activities

Activities are more active than exercises and will involve you doing more than thinking and writing. They are also enclosed by a tinted border. Many of the activities need to involve other people, or to work in a small group. If you are working through this book in conjunction with workshops you could contact other people that you've met there.

If you're working through this book on your own, think about who you know who would help you with some of the activities. Maybe sympathetic friends or relatives, neighbours or colleagues at work? It makes the work more fun and more constructive if two or three friends or colleagues start the book together and give each other support and help with the activities.

Working in a group enables you to:

— share your progress and gain support
— get ideas and encouragement
— gain confidence in the new skills you're developing
— practise and gain feedback
— discuss the results of the exercises you've done on your own.

It is important that you do the activities, so don't be tempted to skip them because it seems a hassle to organise. You do not need to work with the same women all the way through – use the opportunity to get to know as many people as you can.

4 Questionnaires

Questionnaires are used from time to time. They mostly do not require scoring in any way, but are there to raise issues and provoke thought.

5 Examples

The examples are simply there to illustrate the points being made, or to help you into an exercise. The examples are real examples of women currently working and are enclosed in a shaded box. Other examples are given as quotes.

6 Profiles

Profiles are real-life stories from women currently working. These women have written their stories in their own words and given permission for us to use them here. They come from a wide range of backgrounds, work in different ways, have a variety of personal circumstances, and each has her own unique story to tell and points to make. Pay particular attention to the learning points and think about how you can apply them in your situation.

7 Action

You are asked to complete action plans at the end of each section. These are the actions that you are committing yourself to achieving. No one will be checking up on what they are, or whether you've done them; they are your promise to yourself, and you will need to monitor your progress against them.

8 'Me Time'

The final ingredient which we want you to insert for yourself throughout, is 'me time'.

This is because many of us spend most of our lives doing things for work, the house, the children, our families and friends. Our lives fill with duties. This is particularly so for women, who have significantly less time for themselves than men. (*HMSO: Social trends 1987*).

In your 'me time' we want you to give yourself treats. When was the last time you did something that was just for you? It's not self-indulgent, it gives you time to recover and re-energise. If you're out of the habit of treating yourself – try it. We all need it. For example: lock the bathroom door next time you have a bath, and get the kids used to the idea of you having some time to yourself! Add an especially nice bath oil and you're getting the idea! 'Me time' is when you put yourself first for a while.

We haven't indicated when and where your 'me time' should be, but we will be reminding you of its importance from time to time. It may be 10 minutes a day, or an hour a week – whatever you want, but you must do it!

Getting yourself organised

What do you need to do to make the most of this opportunity? Whatever you do, you will need to find:

Chunks of uninterrupted time

Uninterrupted time doesn't have to mean three solid hours – you can break it into chunks; we suggest that half an hour is a minimum to get into it.

— what times are you going to set aside?
— are there any specific times readily available?
— are you going to stop doing something else to make room?
— what can you get others to do to give you some time?

A space where you can relax and concentrate

— can you stay late and use your workplace?
— can you make a corner of the sitting-room your space on Tuesday evenings?
— can you use a library?
— do you have a spare room?
— where can you work?

Help when you get stuck

— where will your help come from?

— what is the attitude of your partner, colleagues, friends, manager, children, parents, organisation?

— do you need to ask for support now?

Getting ready

At various points, you are asked to photocopy pages before you write on them, and also to meet up informally with other women. If you don't have access to a photocopier you will need to write out those pages on separate sheets. So that you can get yourself organised, here is advance notice of these occasions:

Page 11	talk to a close friend or relative
Page 55	talk to two or three others
Page 67	ask a friend or a colleague
Page 70	ask someone who knows you well
Page 71	involve a friend and a person at work
Pages 72-74	photocopy twice
Page 99	talk to two other women
Page 134	photocopy
Page 172-173	meet up with two others
Page 201	photocopy several times
Page 222	meet up with a friend or colleague

Dealing with change

This book is all about making changes. Most people don't like changes, and are reluctant to 'rock the boat' or embrace the changes going on around them.

Write down how you feel about change: *Mostly I instigate change (Temp. furniture, style, decorating; having had a 'locked in' childhood*

Why might you not like change? *Life events however which have to be dealt with alone & come to terms with are traumatic.*

Even if you don't like change, you have probably developed a pattern of coping with change. Some ways of coping are:

— pretend it's not happening √
— insist that the old way is better
— accept it once you've been persuaded
— immediately accept it because it's new
— initiate change yourself ✓
— thrive on it ✓

The Kübler-Ross Change Curve

Elizabeth Kübler-Ross developed the basis of this curve through her work with people undergoing change.

It identifies the stages that most of us go through in response to change both personally, such as a bereavement, and at work, such as redundancy.

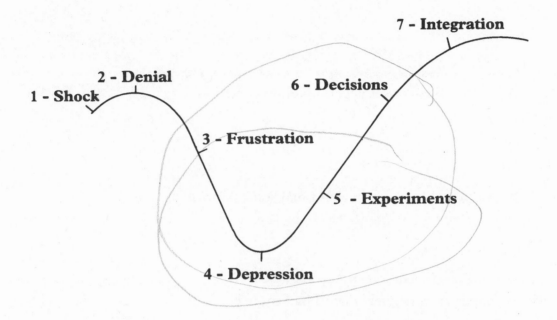

Stage 1 Shock and surprise in response to the event or change. 'I can't believe it!'

Stage 2 Denial of the change and finding ways to prove that it isn't happening. Sticking your head in the sand and reassuring yourself that it isn't really happening. 'I've always done it this way – these new ideas will blow over.'

Stage 3 On the way down, and experiencing anger and frustration. Often a tendency to blame everyone else and lash out at them. Still no acceptance of the change. 'Why pick on me?'

Stage 4 Hitting rock-bottom and experiencing depression and apathy. Everything seems pointless and there is no point in doing anything. 'I'm ready to give up.' Lack of self-confidence.

Stage 5 Stage 4 is so depressing that most of us start to pull ourselves out of it. This is where you will start to try out new things. 'I think I'll have a go at this – after all, anything's better than Stage 4!'

Stage 6 Deciding what works and what doesn't work. Accepting the change and beginning to feel more optimistic and enthusiastic. 'This isn't so bad after all – it actually seems to be working!'

Stage 7 At this stage, you will be integrating the change into your life so it becomes part of your norm – 'The new me!'

Your track record with change

Think of situations where you have had to deal with change, and assess your track record. These could be at home, at work or any other outside-home involvement, such as voluntary work, clubs or societies. Think of at least one situation under each category:

1   A change at home over which I had no control: *Death of spouse*
Seeing as much help as possible, feeling helpless & unsure of everything. taking nothing for granted

2   A change at work over which I had no control: *Moving office accom new boss.*
Prepared for, got involved with, adjusted, kept improving & implementing adjustment

3   A change at home over which I had some control: *Moving house*
Purchasing & selling on my own
Got all info & went for it

4   A change at work over which I had some control: *Moving my desk. Got all info & went for it*

Look back over the four situations you've written down and see how you have dealt with them. Then write in your own response after the example given:

When faced with change that I have no control over, I usually respond by:

Keeping my head down, and feeling very insecure.

Get all the info & help & work thru it (certain amount of trauma)

When faced with change that I have some control over, I usually respond by:

Identifying a way to tackle the change, and preparing myself.

Get all the info, & go for it

When dealing with change, the things I do well are:

Finding out information about the new situation and what I'm supposed to do. ✓

The differences between the way I deal with change at work and change at home are:

I keep quiet at work whilst I make my views known at home.

I make my views known.

Over the next day or two, telephone someone who knows you well and ask them: 'In your opinion, how do I cope with change?' Jot down their reply here:

I pull through eventually - objecting strongly along the way. but trying different coping strategies, working through it

How does their view compare with how you see yourself? Is there a difference between changes at work and changes at home? Perhaps others see that you cope better than you think you do? What can you learn from the feedback that you've received?

I appear much tougher to others + secure than I feel inside

Take a look to see if any of your patterns fit with the Kübler-Ross change curve.

If you are a person who thinks more about the past, it is likely that you will get stuck in feeling depressed (Stage 4) and may tend to slip back to the denial stage (Stage 2). If you are more forward-looking you may be always trying out new ideas (Stage 5) without ever actually moving on to integrate them (Stage 7). Most people have difficulty between the 5th, 6th and 7th Stages.

For example: When Sarah was promoted to Office Supervisor, she went on doing everything she always used to do, on top of her new responsibilities (Stage 2). She ended up very overworked and not initially recognising that she needed to allocate more work to her team. She firstly became frustrated (Stage 3) and then quite depressed (Stage 4) and then she realised that she would need to do something a bit differently (Stage 5). Once she began experimenting, she found the best ways to behave in her new situation. She delegated some of her most familiar tasks, and taught herself how to monitor progress (Stage 6). Once she made her new systems her own, she was fine again (Stage 7).

For example: Sarita is an Assistant Press Officer. She seldom gets depressed but she does spend quite a bit of her time feeling anxious about the future (Stage 3). When she has the chance to take on new work that would help her career she does so with great enthusiasm (Stage 5). But she never seems to finish anything. The more she tries, the more frustrated she gets. She has a great list of ideas to try and when one doesn't work she's ready with the next one. When she looked at the change-curve she said 'That's me – running round in circles from Stage 5 to Stage 3 and back again! I never seem to make it up the final slope.' Now she is trying out one idea at a time and sticking to it longer than usual to check if it really will work.

If you apply your usual pattern to this programme, where is your danger point?

Over enthusiasm & hope, over work, tired, failure, disappointment, seek new approach, run round tread mill again, too many things on at once, all or nothing approach

The phase you'll enjoy most is likely to be:

starting new experiments - (5)

Your objectives

Having read about this Workbook – what about you? You may be clear that you want to get further in your life and work, or you may want to get more out of what you're doing now. You may simply want to take three months to review and revise your priorities in life. Whatever your objectives and reasons, make sure they're your own, and not what you think your partner, your manager, your parents, your organisation or we would want you to write.

Consider these questions before stating your overall objective:

— do you have any specific work or personal goals?

— are you wanting to change or get a job?

— are you wanting more time to do things that you want to do?

— have you got any overall sense of direction?

— do you know what you *don't* want to do?

— do you want to improve your relationships at work and/or at home?

— do you want to change anything about yourself? If so, what?

What are your objectives in working with this book?

I want to find a way of living my life so I don't feel so pushed around

I am ambitious and want to be a Senior Nurse

I want to get my life organised - get rid of all the 'rubbish' I'm carrying around.

I know who I am & how I want to present myself but I lack confidence, & just when I'm getting there I self sabotage. I adopt the I'll do this for now - I'll do it later - which is very tiring & makes me constantly overwhelmed.

I want to do it Now

The luck challenge

When we ask women on courses how they've achieved things in their lives, they often say: 'I was lucky' or 'It was just luck really'.

We believe that this is mostly rubbish! When we ask for anecdotal evidence, we then hear wonderful and inspiring stories of women who:

—   set themselves goals
—   plucked up courage
—   picked brains
—   kept going despite many difficulties
—   made contacts
—   volunteered
—   told people what they wanted
—   made opportunities for themselves
—   refused to give up
—   responded positively to failure.

They had developed the right attitude, and taken the right steps to place themselves in the right place at the right time.

There was usually an opportunity open to them, which they had the courage to grab, and that is the true scale of the 'Luck' that people refer to. When opportunities are there the women who use them are seen as successful. The truly determined don't even wait for opportunities, but stride out positively to make their own.

Most of us say 'it was luck' because it might seem big-headed to say:

—   'I was the best for the job.'
—   'I get on well with people.'
—   'I was determined to make the grade.'
—   'I did my background research very thoroughly.'

It's much easier to say 'I was lucky!' The trouble is that after a while you start believing in lucky breaks and waiting for them to happen. You could wait for ever!

We challenge you to take any achievement which you put down to luck, and will guarantee that luck played a very small part indeed. Your luck was your own effort, determination, skills and experience.

We're not saying that there's no such thing as luck, we're simply suggesting that it has a much smaller part to play than most people credit, and that to a large extent you can make your own luck; we subscribe to this well known definition of luck:

Luck happens when preparation meets opportunity.

This means that you have to do the preparation before you can seize the opportunity! You will, of course, have done this many times in your life already, but from now on be more aware of the amount of control you have over events.

How is the timing for you?

How are you feeling about all this now?

— impatient to get started?

— wishing you'd never decided to do this?

— anxious?

— ready to make changes?

— in the No 5 state again - hopeful experimentation

The timing will never be perfect. A good time is when you feel almost ready for change. You then need a bit of courage to take the plunge. If you wait until you are certain, it may well be too late.

Write down your thoughts and feelings after reading these examples:

Betty	Kim
I'm feeling rather worried right now. It's many years since I did any studying and I hope I'll be able to keep putting aside the time each week. I'm feeling a bit old for all this.	I'm hoping this will unstick me. I've been a plasterer for 5 years now and I'm going nowhere. I'm not quite sure what to expect, but I'm keen to get started.

Already I am remembering who I was before I got stuck. I can see I have a future (I want to be taken seriously & must be more professional at work)

I am afraid of being ridiculed so I don't let people think I serious cos I 'always' meet put downs. How to cope with them. Image, Image, Image.

Summary and action

In this section you've found out about this Workbook and its approach. You've got yourself organised and you've made a start.

Your personal resource bank

Log the points that you want to remember about your response to change.

Action

What actions will you take now to get yourself started?

Here are some suggestions:

— get together with a friend and think of lots of ideas for 'me time'
— clear a corner at home to become your workspace
— talk to your family about the support you want while you're doing this
— give yourself a treat – you've started!

Write yours here:

nr at Session

I will _Sort out all the pieces of paper I am holding for some Doily & adopt a D in now policing._ by (date) _____

I will _Keep a diary of goals & successes._ by _____

I will _talk to family about support I work_ by _____

I will _____ by _____

Profile

Sheila Hesketh
Work Scheduling Officer – British Gas North Western

As the youngest of three children with an ailing father and a mother who seemed to spend most of her life cleaning, I was privileged to be able to stay on at school to take my School Certificate. I wanted it, my parents wanted it (at some sacrifice), so I worked hard and achieved it.

Learning point: Qualifications are important. They give a sense of achievement and build self confidence.

Mother's ambition for me was to be in a 'nice office job' so at 16 that is what I did. It was mundane work, well below my capabilities, but I was only waiting for 'Mr Right' to come along anyway, wasn't I? He did – but he was no millionaire, so I have worked as an 'earner' for all but two of our 36 years of marriage. We had two children with five years between them.

I was, typically, the victim of conditioning until realisation dawned and I cut loose in favour of ambition. My life was a hotch-potch of mundane, menial, sometimes part time jobs until I entered the Gas Industry as a part time waitress in 1970. There I observed others, many with no qualifications, doing 'nice office jobs', so I applied and then realised I was quite good at it.

Learning point: Be aware of conditioning. Be prepared to question the reasons why you do not do things – then 'unpack the childhood baggage' and get going! You do not require all the skills before you apply for the next job up!

I applied for promotion and was successful on two occasions, moving eventually into the world of Training as an instructor on the clerical and administration side. This was the real turning point. I had started further education at night school and progressed to take Institute of Personnel Management (IPM) examinations.

My boss in training encouraged personal development and provided opportunities for it, although I had to learn to ask for what I needed, putting forward my case in a logical manner. I only realised later what a good 'mentor' he was.

At this time I also learned how important appearance is. Advice on dressing for the next job up is now well documented and many of us have learned valuable lessons from colour analysis.

Learning points: Reorganise your time to accommodate study/work needs. Ask those around you for help, sometimes the hardest thing to do.

Find a mentor, someone who is a 'gardener' of people – to help and advise you.

By this time I had met many women who were very frustrated in their jobs. I started a women's network group and a long uphill climb to get some of them to start on their own personal development – and to realise that 'career' and 'ambition' are not bad words for women.

The Women's Network is now well established throughout the whole of British Gas with groups in every region. We meet every other year for a national conference and have a national group which meets twice a year to coordinate activities and ideas. We have a 'voice' in British Gas – a traditionally male industry. There is still a long way to go, but we continue on the way uphill!

Learning point: Helping others also helps you. There is a lot of satisfaction in sharing success together – and self confidence grows. Be active – nothing much happens when you are passive.

Like many other companies British Gas has undergone a number of reorganisations which have had their effect upon the industry and the employees. With a 'flattened' management structure many of us found ourselves competing for fewer positions – at the same grades with increased responsibilities. My staff numbers almost trebled, along with the additional duties, when I was successful in being appointed to my present job. Please – don't ever quote to me 'you can't teach an old dog new tricks'. At 59 I find myself learning new things almost every day! Change is inevitable and a positive approach towards it makes it easier to cope with and adapt to.

Learning point: Learn as much as you can from as many people as you can. Knowledge is power and power is useful providing it is not misused. Think positively – you *can* if you *think* you *can!*

There are always some failures and disappointments along the way. I don't dwell on them. They are always good learning experiences and can often be turned to your advantage. I have only one regret in my working career – I did not achieve the final examination result in the IPM so I have no formal qualifications. (I opted out at the very end because my sister died leaving four children who needed my help). However, I do have the experience of the studying and have found that invaluable in all aspects of my life and career.

Learning point: Don't blame yourself for failure and disappointments. Learn from them and resolve not to repeat them.

Balancing home and work was not too difficult for me. I have a very supportive husband and we cultivated teamwork with our children when I was studying at night school. They took on tasks which helped them to develop into their adult life. My husband and I have almost a complete role reversal which has evolved over the years. He cooks, does the washing, etc. whilst I do all the decorating and repair work. We share the gardening and pay someone to do the housework. With five grandchildren close by, and an active interest in golf, yoga and ten-pin bowling, we lead a very happy life. Our forward plan is well in hand – to enjoy our retirement years together.

Learning point: Have yourself some 'personal' time when you do only what you want to – without feeling guilty about it!

THE WORLD ABOUT YOU

2

Women now have it within their power not simply to move forward as individuals, but to bring to government, business and industry, a set of experiences and perspectives totally different from those which at present control them.

Dr. Rosalind Miles, *Women and Power*

Objective: To alert you to the society and organisation around you, and to the opportunities that are offered

This section is important because:

— events and trends that are going on around you dramatically affect your opportunities

Contents:

— global issues
— women's lives in the UK
— trends in organisations
— your personal power
— how people get recognition
— summary and action
— profile of Gail Cookson

The world about you

The whole world is experiencing dramatic and accelerating change, and you and your plans fit into these larger patterns. Here are four random examples: travel, communications, deforestation, energy production. You can take almost any aspect of our lives and the picture is the same.

Not only are things changing faster, but the whole way we live, the way things are developed and used, is speeding up in an unprecedented way, and there are no signs of a let up.

In this section take a look at what is happening around you, especially at what is happening to women's lives, and what is happening in organisations. If you're not in paid work at the moment, consider the organisations that you're hoping to work for. If you're a one-woman band, consider the business you, or your customers, are in. You may well think 'What's that got to do with me?' as our own surroundings are often taken for granted – we've grown with them, we've adapted, we rarely stop to think about them, and yet they dramatically affect our progress.

Remember the first time you may have visited another country – everything was different, and you may have become acutely aware of things you normally take for granted – for example: how to catch a bus, or how to order a meal. Even the air itself may have made you feel different – more sleepy or more exhilarated. When you consider the environment in which your personal journey takes place, things you've take for granted may give you clues for moving forward.

Global issues

Knowing about global issues can stimulate thoughts, stir up feelings, and motivate you into action. Improved communication means that everyone can become more aware of global issues if they want to. This knowledge can either make people feel overwhelmed and powerless, or galvanise them into action.

Seeing what goes on in the world around you that makes you angry or sad may give you clues about what you want to do with your life, or things you feel energised to do something about.

This Workbook is not the place to start cataloguing all the ailments of the world, so you'll have to decide for yourself which issues you will find out more about, whether it's the deforestation of the tropical rain forests or the treatment of hyperactive children. Whatever you decide – start taking action! After all, the men haven't made such a great job of running things so far! Here is some global information about women to start you off:

Women constitute half the world's population, perform nearly two-thirds of its work hours, receive one tenth of the world's income, and own less than one-hundredth of the world's property.

UN Report

There is increasing evidence of a new determination amongst women, who are less inclined to accept the lives that others decide for them and are wanting to take more control over their own lives.

No longer are women an 'other' knocking at the door to be let into society. Women now have gone beyond this point, reaching a stage where they no longer want to integrate themselves into men's world so much as to reshape the world, make it something better.

Shere Hite

Don't underestimate your influence

Often people feel very strongly about a global issue but also feel totally unable to do anything about it. Keep your eyes and ears open for examples of individual people living ordinary lives, changing big things, little by little, by standing up to be counted, and by acting locally. The influence of local initiatives such as road safety campaigns, rape crisis centres and recycling projects can be inspiring examples of the difference each of us can make – you just need to start!

Never doubt that a small group of committed citizens can change the world, indeed it is the only thing that ever has.

Margaret Mead – Social Anthropologist

Your Global Issues

What are the world-wide issues that you feel strongly about?

Starving children, rises in population

The missapropriation of money by goverment leaders

What do you want to find out about?

What can I do locally?

What are you going to do to start?

Write to Oxfam to discover where my nearest group is

Women's lives in the UK

Here are some facts and trends which are current at the time of writing, to give you food for thought:

— Women constitute 33% of the paid workforce worldwide. Women constitute 44% of the paid workforce in the UK, and this is increasing. 9% of women in the workforce are Black or from minority ethnic groups.

— More than 11 million women are in full- or part-time employment. 44% of women work part-time compared to 8% of men.

— Black and minority ethnic women are three times more likely to be unemployed as white women.

— The UK workforce includes 700,000 (5.7%) disabled women. 1 in 3 of these women have no qualifications. 20% of disabled women are unemployed.

— There is no protection against discrimination on the grounds of sexuality – you can be sacked from your job for being a lesbian.

— 25% of lesbians have experienced at least one violent attack in the last 5 years. 23% of lesbians do not tell anyone about their sexuality in order to avoid harassment.

— Overall, women's earnings are only 72% of men's and Black women earn only 63% of men's earnings. Britain has the highest earnings gap between men and women of all the major countries in the European Union.

— Women are twice as likely as men to be low paid. Homeworkers (most of whom are women) can earn as little as 50p an hour.

— Nearly a third of small businesses are started by women – 150,000 every year.

— Self-employment is growing substantially.

— Women graduates are four times more likely than men to take up employment as teachers and lecturers.

— 22% of women pensioners are on income support, compared to 9% of men.

— The UK Statutory Maternity Benefit is six weeks at 90% of salary, followed by 12 weeks at a reduced rate. This compares with Italy with 14 weeks at 70% of salary and Luxembourg with 16 weeks at 100% of salary.

— 21% of families with dependent children in 1992 were headed by a lone parent. 90% of lone parents are lone mothers.

— In the UK, only 1 in 9 children under 8 years old are provided with formal childcare. The UK and Ireland are the worst countries in Europe in supplying formal childcare for under 8's.

— 70% of women with dependent children work in paid employment.

— Care in the Community has increased pressures on women to look after sick relatives and elderly dependent relatives as well as children, at home.

— Only very few countries recognise paternity leave. The UK doesn't. Denmark gives two weeks. 90% of British men support the introduction of paternity leave.

— Families headed by women now comprise 25% of all households in the world and 20% of households in the UK.

— 70% of divorces are initiated by women.

— More than 25% of households consisted of one person, in 1990.

— Domestic violence constitutes 25% of all reported crime. One in five women experiences domestic violence.

— Women managers are, on average, seven years younger than their male counterparts, and have been with their organisations for a shorter period of time.

— 2.8% of directors and 9.8% of managers in 1994 were women. The percentage of women in management is falling. The most popular jobs for women in management are in personnel and marketing, where they form 33%.

— In 1995, women formed 1% of main board directors.

— Women constitute 19% of members of the House of Commons and 6% of the House of Lords, 8% of senior Civil Servants and 6% of university professors.

— Only one woman director in the UK's top 200 companies is in the most senior job in the company.

— 51.6% of female managers have company cars compared to 61.1% of their male colleagues.

— 76% of clerical and secretarial employees are women.

At the current rate of progression, it will be 500 years before women have equal managerial status in the world, and after that it will be a further 475 years before women hold equal political and economic status.

Sources:

The Daycare Trust – BBC Radio 4 – 1997
The Daily Mail, March 6th 1997
Disabled People and the Labour Market – G.L.A.D. Information Department 1995
News Update – NAWO – March 1997
Queer Bashing – Stonewall – 1996
What Women Want – Body Shop – 1996
Some Facts About Women – EOC – 1996
Women's Rights, Human Rights – Liberty – 1994
National Management Salary Survey – Institute of Management – May 1994
The Equal Opportunities Commission Information Service
Eurostat – Labour Force Survey 1990
New Earnings Survey 1991
Women at the Top – Hansard Society – 1996

Trends in organisations

— Recessions have resulted in ongoing waves of redundancies. People are increasingly appreciative of having any job and fearful of losing the one they have. The concept of a career for life is now obsolete.

— Public sector organisations are having to become more entrepreneurial and even income-generating.

— Increased use of new technology, such as e-mail and the Internet.

— Many organisations are reducing the numbers of full time employees and instead are contracting out work to freelance people and/or increasing the numbers of part-time employees.

— The 'Opportunity 2000' campaign is raising awareness of women's career issues in some organisations.

— There is a growing acceptability of ideas from the environmental or 'green' movement.

— More flexible working patterns such as job-sharing, term-time-only working and flexitime are becoming more common.

— There is an increasing influence from the European Union. In addition, the removal of trade barriers between EU countries resulted in an increase in opportunities for working in Europe. Equally, there are increased opportunities for people from other EU countries to work in the UK.

— Greater financial accountability is being required from individual departments, units and managers.

— The number of young people aged 16–25 is falling by 1.4 million between 1987 and 2000. Women represent an under-developed source of labour for employers.

— Large companies are increasingly working towards the following formula: that within 4 years half as many people will be paid twice as much for working three times as hard. This means that there is a need for individuals who:

  – are able to cope with periods of unemployment

  – retain their employ*ability* rather than their employment

  – consider making their own work

  – accept the need for reskilling and retraining

  – accept responsibility for their own development

  – are able to cope with personal finances such as personal pensions etc.

Spot the new initiatives in your organisation!

Such as:
— job sharing
— introduction of e-mail
— involvement in NVQs (National Vocational Qualifications)
— open learning centres
— support for Open University courses
— women-only courses
— career break schemes

Note down others that you discover:

What does it all mean to you?

Considering all these facts and trends:
Are there any others that you've observed?

Do any of these facts surprise you or do they confirm what you already know?

What opportunities are offered to you by these facts and trends?

What threats are posed to you by these facts and trends?

How will they influence the important people in your work life?

How will they influence the important people in your personal life?

Take a look at your own organisation

In a huge and diverse organisation some of the general culture may affect you greatly, or have only a small effect. In a small organisation it may affect every aspect of your work. It's likely that the day-to-day culture of your own workplace has a dramatic effect on your morale, and your opportunities for change. Have a think through these aspects:

What is the structure of your organisation?

Are there particular areas where people get promoted quickly? If so – which?

What is highly valued, eg: loyalty, bright ideas, independence of thought, long service, attention to detail?

What is the general attitude to people outside your workplace?

Which sort of people hold the influence, eg: people who make the boss laugh, people who have been there a long time?

Is there an inner circle of people who hold the influence? If so – why? How can an outsider get to know them?

What are the anecdotes that are told fondly about the organisation or about past members of the organisation?

Where is the organisation going? Is there a sense of direction?

What do you know about the people who use your organisation's goods/services?

Who decides what happens in your workplace?

Overall, how is the culture of your own place of work affecting you and your ability to achieve your ambitions?

Your personal power

You do not operate in a vacuum. The opportunities that are open to you, the way you are perceived, your ability to influence people, your ability to make things happen, the chances of having your own values met, are all influenced by the culture of your organisation.

Very often, when this subject is mentioned on courses, people wrinkle their noses and look very wary. Organisational culture, and the use of influence inside organisations, is often assumed to be about playing office politics, playing games, or becoming another rat in the rat race. These represent the negative side and make judgements about power. In the next part of this section, look at some of the issues in an entirely neutral way and then decide for yourself at the end whether you want to ignore them or use them positively.

Organisational culture and the use of power, in themselves, are entirely neutral. They are the oil that lubricates the cogs of the organisation.

Your personal power is your ability to influence others

You probably have more ability to influence what's going on around you than you think! If you ask someone to do something, and they do it, then clearly you had the ability to influence that person – you were using your personal power in that situation.

Your power takes several forms. Here are the four main ones that are found inside organisations. If you're not currently working inside an organisation, think of any voluntary group, society, or social club that you're involved in.

1 Formal authority
This is the power invested in you by your job title. Anyone doing your job would have your formal authority. It manifests itself in the right to make decisions, and the right to insist (sometimes called 'pulling rank').

2 Expertise
This is the power given to you by your specialist knowledge, skills, experience and qualifications. The more exclusive the expertise and the more useful in your workplace, the more power it gives you.

3 Resource control
Someone may do what you ask them to do because you control their access to something that they want. This power is the control of physical, financial or informational resources. For example: allocation of car parking spaces, access to the stationery cupboard, access to people, whether you tell everything that happened at the union meeting, etc. People in relatively lowly hierarchical positions often have a great deal of resource control power, but the most valued resources are usually money and information.

4 Interpersonal skills
This is the power you have in the way you get on with people, your ability to persuade and to build good quality relationships, your assertiveness. This is often considered to be the most potent form of power.

Your power questionnaire

The following questionnaire is not designed to be scored in any way, but is designed to help you think about the power you have, and although it was designed for people in paid employment, the same factors have influence in a voluntary group or a family:

Formal authority

— Do you have the formal right (say, in your job description) to make decisions, other than trivial ones?

— Do other people need your approval before they take action?

— Do you supervise someone else's work?

— Do your decisions significantly affect important aspects of your department's work long-term?

— Does your manager typically support your decisions and not overrule them?

— Do you encounter any resistance to your right to make decisions, supervise others, and give approval, from subordinates, peers, more senior people? (If you do, this suggests a reduction in your power which you may need to do something about).

Expertise

— Does it take a year or longer to learn to do your job adequately?

— Do you need a qualification to do your job?

— What is the highest qualification in your field? – do you have it?

— Are you the only person who can do your job?

— If you were to leave, would they have difficulty in replacing you?

— Does your knowledge and skill relate to a major aspect of the department's work?

— Do people frequently consult you and follow your advice?

— Do more senior people clearly show that they value your contribution?

Resource control

Can you give or withhold access to the following resources?

— money

— information

— ideas

— training

— other people

— computers

— perks

— time

Add any others that you control:

Interpersonal skills

— Are you on good terms with a number of people across different departments and hierarchical levels?

— Do people confide in you?

— Are you good at speaking at meetings?

— Are you an active listener? Do you make sure you have understood the other person's point of view?

— Do you make sure that other people take your views seriously when it matters to you?

— Do you avoid being either passive or aggressive in formal or informal discussion with others at work?

— Can you hold the attention of a group or larger audience?

Material used, with permission, from Dr Margaret Ryan's work in *Power and Influence in Organisations* published by The Training Agency.

Your power net

On the next page is a diagram of your own power net. Put your own name in the bubble in the centre, as shown in the example below. In the other bubbles put the names of individual people who have an important effect on your work. They may be higher or lower than you in the hierarchy, and either inside or outside your organisation. Use the names of individuals and not whole departments, because your power is based on individual relationships.

You may want to re-draw the diagram on a separate piece of paper if you feel comfortable with a different shape. Add extra bubbles if you need to.

Using the four categories of power outlined on the previous page, assess which sorts of power you are using in your relationship with each person.

Rachel's Power Net

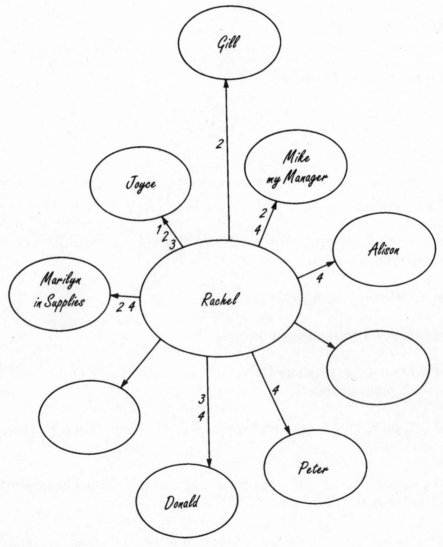

1 **Formal Authority**
2 **Expertise**
3 **Resource Control**
4 **Interpersonal Skills**

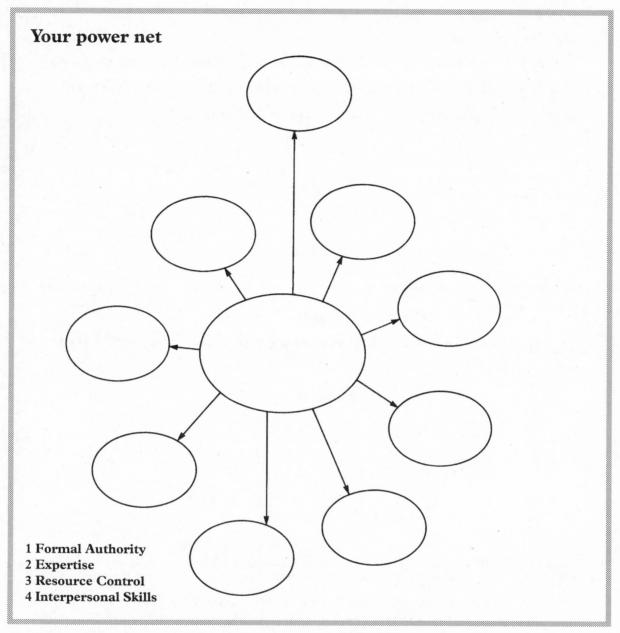

Your power net

1 Formal Authority
2 Expertise
3 Resource Control
4 Interpersonal Skills

You can also do the exercise the other way round and consider what form of power people are using to influence you!

What does it mean?

What have you discovered about how you use your own power? Are you using all your sources of power effectively? Most women underestimate their ability to influence things around them, so you might not have done yourself justice in this exercise. Have another think!

Most women's power is based on using interpersonal skills, as women tend to have less formal authority and restricted access to obtaining expertise.

If you've found that you're relying heavily on your interpersonal skills then you're doing well. All the research on the skills needed in the workplace in the future points to the increased importance of good interpersonal skills and the devaluing of the use of authority. This could be good news for you as long as you keep your skills polished up and look for opportunities to build up your other sources of power.

Make your notes here:

I was quite surprised to see how much power my knowledge of computers gives me. I never thought of it like that. I'm also relying very heavily on my interpersonal skills to get things done. Thinking about power made me think of physical power too.

Which situations do you want to change?

I'm going to speak at meetings more and make myself more visible. I need to polish up my assertiveness generally.

If you're working through this in a group or with a friend, get together to compare notes on this exercise and see if you've underestimated yourself in your power net, and bear in mind that power operates in families too.

The impression of power

Having the formal authority, expertise or resource control is not always enough. **Being seen to have it is important**. Other people's willingness to be influenced hinges largely on their perception of you, or the impression you create. In other words – your credibility.

For example: At a meeting Anne may have the most expertise on a particular subject, be the most up-to-date and have the most relevant information on it. Also at the meeting is Tina who knows a great deal less about the subject, but creates the impression that she is a real expert. Tina's ability to influence the meeting may be as great, if not greater, than Anne's, because Tina has more credibility. Sadly, unless Anne does a better job on the image she creates, her organisation may not realise the value of her expertise until after she's left.

So don't assume that people remember your expertise, respect your formal authority, recognise your resource control and value your interpersonal skills.

It's up to you to be proud of what you've got going for you and use it positively!

How people get recognition

If you're waiting to get promoted, move sideways, or change your job in any way, it is important to work out a further aspect of how things happen in organisations.

Research by Harvey Coleman (ex-IBM) across a number of large organisations identified three factors that determine whether someone is promoted or not:

1 **Performance** – the reality of how good your work actually is.

2 **Image** – the impression you create about yourself and your work. We all know of people who were overlooked for promotion because while their work was actually good they gave the impression of being confused, or unable to cope, or not interested in promotion.

3 **Exposure** – whether people know of you. This means raising your profile, becoming more visible and building your contacts. You may do a great job, have a great image, but if the right people don't know that you exist – you won't get promoted.

The contribution of each of these factors to people being promoted were:

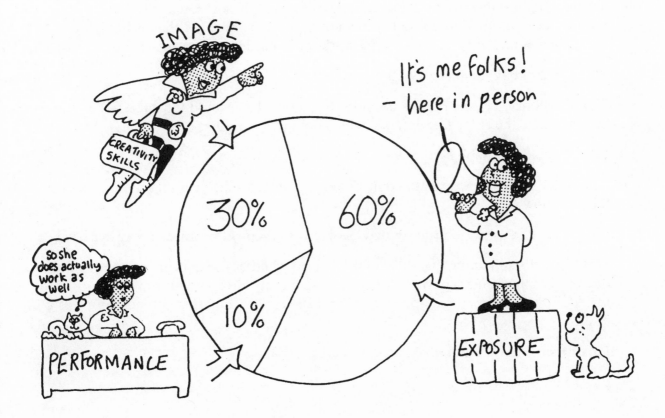

It may seem outrageous that the quality of your work contributes only 10% towards getting you promotion or recognition, but if you're in an organisation where everyone does a good job the other two factors assume greater and greater significance.

There are usually several people who are capable of doing the job – the person who gets it also has her image and exposure working for her. These statistics are not saying 'Don't bother to do a good job' but they are saying:

'Do a good job, but don't think anyone's going to promote you for it!'

'Do a good job, but put some effort into building your image, and increasing your exposure as well.'

These statistics go a long way towards explaining:

The Flossie trap

There is no significance in calling this particular trap after 'Flossie', so our apologies to anyone called Florence or Flossie, but it is a phenomenon which affects women much more than men.

There is usually a Flossie in every organisation.

There may be several.

There can be a Flossie in a family too.

Flossies are male and female, but are more usually female.

Flossie is the person who thinks that promotion comes with doing a good job. She believes that if she works well enough and hard enough, someone will notice and reward her. If promotion doesn't come along, she may interpret that as implying she's not working well enough, so she works even harder and better.

Flossie is holding the place together.

Flossie will never be promoted, because the whole place would fall apart – it's much better to take the risk with someone who's not indispensable.

Flossie is indispensable.

At home Flossie believes that people do appreciate her – it's just that they're too busy to show it.

Flossie is often asked to train up new people who then get promoted over her head.

As Flossie doesn't know that 90% of the reason whether she gets promoted or not is due to her image and exposure, she doesn't make any efforts to improve her interpersonal skills and her appearance, and she regards building contacts as a waste of time.

Flossie can end up bitter, frustrated and exhausted.

Flossie ends up stuck.

Your Flossie rating

Have you ever been a Flossie? (Most of us have!)

Are you a Flossie now?

Do you want to do anything about it?

If so – what?

Learn to say No

Delegate

Tell my boss what my aspirations are

Go home on time

Summary and action

In this section you've looked at just some of the things that are going on around you and begun to assess where the opportunities lie for a change.

Further optional reading

Charles Handy – *Beyond Certainty* – published by Arrow Books
Robin Norwood – *Women who love too much* – published by Arrow Books
Dale Spender – *Nattering on the Net* – published by Spiniflex

Action

What action are you going to take to make the most of the opportunities open to you?

Here are some suggestions:

— find out about any open learning facilities in my organisation or area
— find out more about being self-employed or going on contract
— build up my contacts in other parts of the organisation
— join Friends of the Earth
— decide whether I'm happy being a Flossie or not
— speak out about how I feel about cruelty to animals
— refer to the Appendix for other books to read

I will _____ by_____

I will _____ by_____

I will _____ by_____

I will _____ by_____

Profile

Gail Cookson
Director, Cookson Creative

I have been working for nearly 15 years in six different organisations and many more different jobs. My first job was as a Personal Assistant to a Director in a life assurance company. I am currently running my own direct marketing consultancy. The path to this position was neither straight nor obvious!

Learning point: Make the patchwork quilt of a CV appear planned and relevant – turn it into a portfolio career.

Personal achievement has always been important to me. I was the youngest of three and the first to get to university in my family. On graduating, I decided I wanted to be an auctioneer. A small amount of research uncovered a major problem. I would have to pay my employers, and not the other way round. Auctioneering it seemed, was for those who could afford it!

So I took the easy option, and became a secretary, first in insurance and then in a major training organisation. I then spent at least two years trying not to be a secretary!

Learning point: Easy options are seldom easy.

After sending up the smoke signals, finally I was promoted, but this was not without its trials. I was placed in a job by a director whose departmental manager had other ideas. She didn't want me!

Learning point: Learn positive things from negative experiences.

However, another head of department did want me! At last I felt I had arrived in the right job where I could develop my skills. I discovered I had a good eye for detail, could get my mind round complex issues like new legislation and liked looking at things from the customer's point of view. In short, I developed an interest in marketing.

Learning point: Learn your strengths and weaknesses and play to your strengths.

After a further two happy years in the job, I decided to move to help set up a much smaller organisation, again in training. It did not work. Everyone is allowed one Dodo on their CV.

Learning point: Check out the facts before changing jobs. Work out what size of organisation you feel comfortable in.

After 15 months of trying to make it work, I moved to a national charity as their Direct Mail Manager. I had a caring boss who kept developing me and when she left I was promoted to her job. This involved managing a department of 10 very independent people (9 women and 1 man). Unfortunately, my new boss gave me no support, nor sadly, could I learn much from him. Sometimes you have to learn to cut your losses.

Learning point: Always try and work for someone you can learn from. Learn which battles are important and which are not.

I then moved to a large direct marketing agency, where I gained lots of experience in dealing with different clients and their marketing problems. The work was hard, the variety was stimulating and I learnt a lot. In the year I became a board director, I also became a mother and I was also made redundant. They are not entirely connected.

In 1991, the recession was really biting marketing services companies. The agency's financial problems were precipitated by the problems of the parent company and I was given the 'chance' to bail out. One day I had a job, the next I did not. I had a nine month old baby and I was the major breadwinner in the family. The next few months were very difficult, doing the round of headhunters, writing to contacts, networking, going for interviews.

Then the phone call came. The head of fundraising of a major charity needed some help desperately with their direct marketing campaigns for the autumn. A twelve week contract ended about two years later. Another call, from someone I nearly went to work for a few years before, resulted in more work. We set up Cookson Creative to offer direct marketing services to charities. I have a handful of clients which keeps me ticking over.

Learning point: It's not just what you know but also who you know.

However, this is not the end of the story. Having done my own thing for two years, I am shortly going to join another agency. My reasons for this are that whilst I enjoy looking after clients, I don't relish finding and pitching for them. The new agency offers me the chance to do what I am good at and let others do the things I am not good at.

A friend who is a Personnel Manager once said to me that looking for a job in the current climate is like looking for a space in a car park. You go round and round and round, you miss a few spaces to other cars ahead of or behind you and then suddenly out of the blue that space appears.

KNOWING YOURSELF

3

I wonder if I've been changed in the night? Let me think: was I the same when I got up this morning? I almost think I can remember feeling a little different. But if I'm not the same, the next question is, 'Who in the world am I?' Ah, that's the great puzzle.

Lewis Carroll, *Alice in Wonderland*

Objective: To enable you to make the most of yourself

This section is important because:

— understanding where you are now helps you take the next step
— learning from your experiences moves you onwards
— identifying your values clarifies your goals
— letting go of old patterns helps you think more freely about the future

Contents:

— being a woman
— being your age
— being your race and colour
— being with or without a disability
— becoming an experiencing person
— your values
— your attitude
— summary and action
— profile of Sandra Benjamin
— food for thought

Knowing yourself

To think about moving you need to know where you are! Are you:
- ✓ discovering that the path you're on is a cul-de-sac?
- ✓ at a new beginning, taking the first steps?
- ✓ at the top of a hill, surveying the view and wondering 'What now?'
- — at a crossroads and wondering which way to go?
- — in a Rolls Royce purring along easily?
- ✓ in an old banger that may give out any time now?
- — going in totally the wrong direction?
- ✓ soaking your feet in a bucket of water and hoping the pain will go away?
- ✓ out of breath watching the others go by?
- ✓ on a superb plateau, going nowhere?
- Yes having fun, hoping it will last for ever and knowing it won't?
- No trudging along and doing OK, but welcoming a bit of company on the way?

Wherever you are you have this Workbook because you are a woman wanting to change. *Yes, definitely*

Being a woman

As very few people have changed their sex, it's not likely you'll know what it is to be a man. If you have changed your sex to become a woman you will already have thought a lot about the questions that follow. Otherwise, being a woman is all you've known.

How does being a woman affect your life?

What are the best aspects of being a woman?
Give examples of qualities, experiences, opportunities, and conditioning:

I can express my emotions, be creative, wear pretty clothes or be totally messed up. I am warm & caring. I am a mother, I support people. I am a homemaker. I have made a family & made many things possible for them, I support my children even Nick. I have the arts I support by example

---

What are the worst aspects?
Give examples of closed doors, prejudice, lack of opportunity and conditioning:

I soon become a flossie, I have a fast mind & have to pretend cos most men want to be better than women. so I act the fool Women who are not 'beautiful' have a hard time. you have to keep at it. There is always something to do for someone else & tiredness is a enemy in every sphere — you have to keep up

---

How does your sexuality (eg. heterosexual, lesbian, bisexual, transsexual etc.) affect your life?

I always found it easy to attract men, so when widowed suddenly I was convinced I'd soon find another partner. I found many - but they thought/assumed I was desperate for sex.) As a young woman I always had mentors & men friends, my marriage was secure. As an older woman I find I am discarded as old. I am the same age as my boss's mother & have had to put him at ease with this. Similarly many of my co workers as as old as my children & look on my as them, bringy problems etc.
When I awoke from having my breast totally removed I was mortified - I had not realised this wd happen & the elderly general surgeon had no notion of what he had done. I held me with contempt for not thanking him for saving my life. With all my femininity I had to life/ I fought hard to eventually have reconstruction - poor, but better nothing

Being your age

Usually the first thing people notice about other people is what sex they are. The next things they notice are age, race, and whether the person has a disability.

Look at age first. In these examples the two women's pathways are very different because of their ages.

Aloun

I am 23, single and keen to move along quickly. I am working hard to pass my banking exams and can see career steps clearly ahead. I know I need a wide range of experience of different aspects of other work too. There are quite a few other women ahead of me on the path; I feel the opportunities are opening up a bit more.

Mary

I am 46, and back working after a career break of 14 years. I'm building up my confidence again. There were no facilities for me to keep up to date with my work. In my late 30s I felt really unclear about the work I wanted to do in the future, but now I'm sure of what I want to do. I have no illusions about the prejudice that I face as a woman of 46, especially as I've been working part time, but I'm determined to get on. I have better chances than women did 20 years ago. The next generation of returners will get an even better deal as organisations get their acts together. I feel as though I've been on a plateau for a long time.

The significance of your age

The numbers in these boxes are groupings of ages. Write your name in the appropriate box for your age; in addition, think of at least six people who are important to you and write their names in the appropriate boxes for their ages.

AGE CHART

		Over 63 Me Tom
43 – 49 Davy – Owlyny	50 – 56 Carol	57 – 63 Janire Me · Carol
22 – 28	29 – 35 Calrinel Consolidahn Sarah (Jolonal – review) JB Consolidah	36 – 42 ~~Sarah~~ Peter JN
0 – 7	8 – 14	15 – 21

Research shows that people have different needs and wishes in the different stages of their lives. There are three types of stages and each stage usually lasts about seven years. They are not exact to the day or even to the year. Understanding the general flavour of a stage can help explain why some people behave the way they do and why things that are important to you at one stage may not be so important to others who are older or younger.

Knowing about the stages means you can:

- realise you're not alone
- go with the flow of the stage you are in
- be pleased and enjoy a stage when it's good
- know it won't last for ever when it's difficult!
- catch up with things you missed out on last time you were in this stage
- see ahead to the next stage

The Outgoing Stages   0 – 7 years   22 – 28 years   43 – 49 years

Finding your feet may seem an appropriate expression for a three year old, but it is just as likely that a woman of 44 may be feeling that she is just finding her feet again.

In these stages people are going out into the world, doing new things, taking new steps, making changes. These stages need energy and enthusiasm both from the person herself and from those close to her.

The Consolidating Stages   8 – 14 years   29 – 35 years   50 – 56 years

In these stages, people are more settled at home or at work. They have a better idea of who they are, where they are and where they are going. Don't worry if you are the exception! In these stages people deepen their work experience, get more qualifications and become established.

The Reviewing Stages   15 – 21 years   36 – 42 years   57 – 63 years

In these stages, people are wondering who they are, where they are going, what there is for them to do next. The teenage years are typical of these stages. Women in the 36 – 42 and 57 – 63 ages often remark that they feel just as challenged as they did in their teens – and just as misunderstood! For mothers, the 36 – 42 stage may be when they return after a career break. For childless women it's a last chance to have children.

After 63
Research shows that the time after 63 does not fall into the three stages given above. People over 63 describe it as 'free time' because they are frequently free of the need to work. Equally among those still working there is evidence of major initiatives being taken by women in their 70s. Women in their 70s and 80s and in some cases, their 90s, start new hobbies, travel to new places and change their ways of living.

Making the most of the stage you're in

Janet: When I looked at the chart and discovered that my daughter at 17, my mother at 60, and myself at 38 are all in the reviewing stage, I could see why at the moment life is a bit difficult. Having brought up my three children, I am ready to make a substantial change in my life. I am looking out for activities which will boost my confidence. I feel rather as I did when I left school – like being in a first job. I realise that I have a lot to offer and am taking stock of my skills and abilities so that I can give myself a push.

Gisela: I'm 24, have an HNC and have been working here for 2 years. I'm feeling settled into my job now, and am impatient to take some strides. I've got lots of ideas and am keen to get on with my life. I share a house with another woman and two blokes – which my parents consider slightly bizarre – and we all enjoy a good time. I've got a lot going for me and I'm determined to make a go of things. I like being in engineering and want to make it my career. I'd like to have a family sometime, but not for ages yet.

Assess your stage and write down how it influences you and your relationships with the other people in your life:

I am definately in the reviewing stage

The children are in the consolidating stage

Carol is reviewing

Knowing yourself

To think about moving you need to know where you are! Are you:
— discovering that the path you're on is a cul-de-sac?
— at a new beginning, taking the first steps?
— at the top of a hill, surveying the view and wondering 'What now?'
— at a crossroads and wondering which way to go?
— in a Rolls Royce purring along easily?
— in an old banger that may give out any time now?
— going in totally the wrong direction?
— soaking your feet in a bucket of water and hoping the pain will go away?
— out of breath watching the others go by?
— on a superb plateau, going nowhere?
— having fun, hoping it will last for ever and knowing it won't?
— trudging along and doing OK, but welcoming a bit of company on the way?

Wherever you are you have this Workbook because you are a woman wanting to change.

What does it mean to you to be the colour/race that you are?

How has it affected your life so far?

What doors are open or closed as a result?

How relevant is your colour/race to the way you want your life to develop?

How do you feel about people not of your race and colour?

How do these feelings affect your relationships with people not of your race and colour?

Being with or without an impairment

An impairment is the loss of a physical, sensory or mental function or loss or partial loss of one or more organs or limbs. Many impairments are hidden. It may mean having a severe impairment or having a minor impairment, such as being short-sighted, which may stop you getting some jobs. Being physically different in any way affects the way people are treated. Disability is the loss or limitation of opportunity to take an equal part in society. The questions that follow are designed for everyone to consider; not just disabled women:

> **What does it mean to you to be a person with or without an impairment?**
>
> Our society from children classifies us by impairment, everyone has an impairment of some sort

> **How has it affected your life so far?**
>
> I have adjed

> **What doors are open or closed to you as a result?**

> **How relevant is having or not having an impairment to the way you want your life to develop?**
>
> None

> **How do you feel about disabled people?**
>
> Having worked with disabled people the person inside is not disabled

> **How do these feelings affect your relationships with disabled people?**
>
> no problem

Overcoming prejudice

Your sex, sexuality, age, race, colour and level of impairment all have an impact on the people you meet. The degree of impact varies according to the degree of prejudice you hold and meet. When prejudice continues over a period of time, people change their behaviour to overcome it, fight it or give in to it.

To overcome prejudice what parts of your own behaviour do you want to change, if and when you encounter prejudice on account of:

Being a woman

~~I think as~~ I want to deal with men on equal Terms, not act as they think I should

---

Your sexuality

As above

Your age

Remind myself of my tremendous past achieve which it is very likely they will never get the chance to emulate.

Your race or colour

Continue to feel confident, show I'm just like you

Your level of physical ability or impairment

Its not my problem

Anything unusual about you, eg: being very tall

Its not my problem

Becoming an experiencing person

Becoming a fully experiencing person means:

- learning from your experience
- taking the risk involved in being open to life
- having a positive attitude to life
- regarding failure as an opportunity to learn and grow
- actively changing and growing
- learning something new from every year of your life, rather than experiencing the same year over and over again
- meeting every new situation afresh without old preconceptions or rules affecting you
- being an independent thinker; thinking things out for yourself instead of accepting other people's views
- having a healthy curiosity about your past and what you can learn from it to help you in the future

The following exercise exploits your healthy curiosity and extends your process of learning from everything that has happened to you.

This is your life

Use the chart on the next page to map out the events that have happened in your life so far. People usually remember more if they start now and go backwards, so start with your age now and work backwards, just putting a key word or two for each event until you reach your earliest memory. Do it briskly without going into too much detail. If you want more room transfer this on to a bigger sheet of paper.

Here is a list of events from other women, to spark off thought:

started school	went back to work after break
blamed for something not my fault	changed job
unhappy at school	met Paul
fall in love	bought house/car
first kiss/sexual experience	got married/divorced
left school	trip to India
Mum died	accident/ill health
decided not to have children	child born

Events can be:

- something you remember for no specific reason
- happy or sad
- fearful, funny or embarrassing
- success or failure
- challenging
- new or repetitious
- very short experiences, anything from a chance remark that sticks in your head, to a summer holiday
- life changing or insignificant

Some people find it helpful to do this exercise in more than one go. You'll probably
end up with between 20 and 40 events.

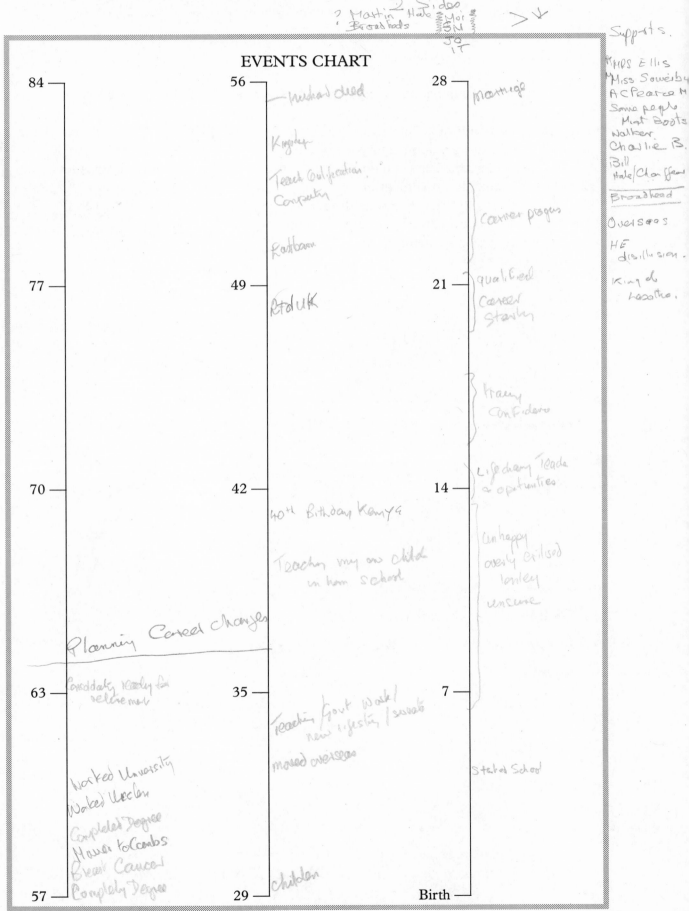

EVENTS CHART

Tracking down the themes

Look at the chart as if it were someone else's and pick out the themes. Timing is a theme and a good place to start.

What major events have you experienced earlier or later than most people?

eg:
- — death of a close friend or relative *Later*
- — taking responsibility for others
- — notable achievements
- — gaining qualifications *avenny*
- — experiencing serious illness
- — marriage/birth/divorce *later*
- — puberty/menopause

Have a look for other themes. What strikes you most as you look at your chart?

lonay & unhappy childhood
supported & overcame this
Back to them ! ie alone
+ being supported

Always been . someone there
to help me.
show me a different lifestyle
+ path

What themes or threads run through your life?

having relationships with the same type of person

feeling anxious ✓

putting myself last ✓

always felt confident, got every job I applied for
really went for everything I wanted

We live our lives forwards but we can only understand them backwards.

Søren Kierkegaard

What are the key turning points?

[handwritten] Taking stock & realising I had to change
Tracy, leaving home, marriage, overseas,
teaching; general degree ✓

What do you see that you would like to let go of?
eg: themes, relationships that are not helping you, ties that are binding you to the
past, humiliations, resentments.

*[handwritten] My childhood ... everything before, & leave home ... the ... to ...
living in the wrong 'dimension' ... to let it happen again ...
... wealthy   needn't put myself down
I will always have money
Someone will always be there for me*

How do you rate yourself in terms of success/failure?

*[handwritten] I always achieve what I set out to do. I had to to
get through my childhood & it has been a useful life tool*

What have you learnt from this exercise?

[handwritten] I'm incrediblly strong, capable, and successful

Time to treat yourself?

This section is hard work. Is this a good time to have some 'me time'? Give yourself
a treat to keep your energy going.

Your values

Your approach to life is based on a set of beliefs that you have acquired over the course of your life so far. Some of these will be truly yours and some may have been acquired from the environment you have lived in. All your decisions are based on what you value. Values are your beliefs, and give you the criteria by which you measure things.

Very often, when people say 'I can't ...' what they really means is 'I don't choose to ...'. You are making lots of choices about your life all day, every day:

— in the way you choose to behave
— in the way you respond or react to situations
— in the priorities you place on relationships and activities
— in the way you spend your money
— in the way you spend your time
— in the way you relate to the rest of the world
— in the way you think and feel about yourself

If you are indecisive, then even choosing *not* to choose also affects the way you spend your life, so there's no avoiding your own influence! The way you make these day-to-day split-second choices is strongly influenced by what matters to you and what you believe in – that is, your values.

Knowing your values tells you what you want to do, don't want to do, are likely to enjoy doing or feel strongly about.

Values change over time, ie: as you get older, and/or as circumstances change. For example, starting work, having children, being left alone.

Values relate to the four different areas of your life – the world, work, relationships and yourself. All these areas overlap, may be in conflict, and may have common denominators. For example – valuing working for the community versus wanting or needing to make a lot of money may create a dilemma.

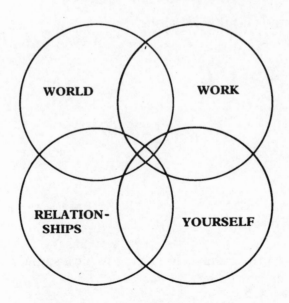

What do you value?

What matters to YOU? What is important? What do you value?

Write down the things you value – use the prompt column to give you ideas – or cover it up if you wish to be left free to find your own ideas.

For the world

Prompts

pollution free
peace
no cruelty to children
everyone with food and water
free political systems
stop greenhouse effect
no cruelty to animals

At work

environment – I will never again work without windows.

position/respect!

be appreciated

responsibility

Prompts

a job
money
challenge & interest
responsibility
travel
working with people
variety of tasks
producing a product/service I value

In your relationships

Solid. self possessed
intelligence
background
strength. physical emotional leaders
to be appreciated for who &
what I am.

Prompts

honesty
someone special
children of my own
shared values
sense of humour
security
to be valued as me

For yourself

femininity
clean, smell nice
grooming
polish
beauty
appearance
etiquette
things done right
a lovely home

organisation paramount

Creating Beauty
helping people to achieve
their aims.
achieving my own

Prompts

sense of humour ✓
peace of mind ✓
following a spiritual path ✓
time to dig the garden ✓
good health ✓
a nice car ✓
house decorated to my taste ✓
having self respect ✓
time to read a book ✓

Meeting values raises energy

When your values aren't being met, it gives rise to dissatisfaction, complaints and niggles, and your energy drains away.

When your values are being met, it brings satisfaction and good feeling, and your energy rises. Values are so personal that no two people have the same lists. There are no right values or wrong values, only your values.

Sharing values

Some people find it easier to share personal things such as values with people they are really close to. Others prefer to share with people they don't know so well.

Sharing has the advantages that you:

— become clearer about your own ideas

— pick up hints and tips from others

— think about and assess what you've written

There is no need to get very heavy about it – even though values are a serious personal issue. Get together with, or telephone two or three other women and share your ideas. Then add any new ideas to your list.

Make notes of any points raised by your thinking about values:

Prioritising your values

Once you've identified your values, prioritise them on the chart on the next page, in terms of how important they are to you.

	I **MUST** HAVE...	I WOULD LIKE TO HAVE...	IT WOULD BE NICE TO HAVE...
WORLD	everythg in harmay People playing the Boat, homesty & Justice. Kindness, considerate helping & shaving spirituality	←	←
WORK	team work Team spirit helping & sharing honesty fairness support respect, consideration	←	←
RELATION-SHIPS	A person of total integrity, Kindness, considerate recognises beauty in nature etc Strength & leaderd	←	←
MYSELF	everywhere lists organised lists, plan goals PEOPLE support unconditional Love	←	←

Are you fulfilled?

On the previous page, tick your values that are being met at the moment.

If you have values in the 'I **must** have' section which aren't being met, then these may give you the clues about the goals that you want to set for the future.

It may seem a bit overwhelming to have values in the 'I **must** have' column for the world, as it may be daunting to think of tackling world hunger or pollution. Acknowledge the values now and wait till later to think about how you will meet them.

If people have large numbers of unfulfilled values in the 'I **must** have' section, they may respond by:

— becoming bitter and cynical
— gaining the drive and determination to do something about it
— daydreaming wistfully about what might have been
— complaining that life isn't fair

How do you feel about your fulfilled values?

OK

How do you feel about your unfulfilled values?

29 May 05 - I am looking to do something about them

Which unfulfilled values do you want to do something about?

Your attitude

Your attitude to life develops out of your experiences, and the way you think and feel, and is THE KEY to your success.

Here are some examples of positive and negative attitudes which will greatly affect the outcome of situations. Some of them affect situations so dramatically that they become self-fulfilling prophecies:

28 May 01

I am feeling very positive

NEGATIVE	POSITIVE
Where's the catch?	Where's the opportunity? ✓
I'm better than you	I am equal to you ✓
This will never work	I'll make this work ✓
I'm not worth this	I am worth this ✓
I've heard it all before	What can I learn here? ✓
I can't do this	I can do this ✓
What's wrong with this?	What's right with this?
I'll make a fool of myself	I'll learn something ✓
I'm too old	I'm not too old ✓

I am 8 years younger physically

YOUR ATTITUDE COLOURS HOW PEOPLE SEE YOU

Your attitude can warm the space between you and other people, and help them respond to you more positively. Optimistic and energetic people are promoted in preference to cynical and inflexible people. So – keep the drive and energy that you have going. If you've lost it – take action to find it again.

YOUR ATTITUDE IS THE FILTER THROUGH WHICH YOU SEE YOUR LIFE. YOU MAY NOT WANT IT ROSE-COLOURED, BUT MAKE IT POSITIVE!

How do you know what your attitude is?
Of course, some of your attitudes change depending on your relationships, the time of year, your time of the month, your level of motivation, the reward in view, or changing events.

What would you say are your basic, underlying attitudes?

dissappointment, frustration, dry bitter, loss of faith, loneliness, lack of trust.

28 May 01
Having got treatment now I realise I had a problem I didn't know about. I will feel better.

Head tapes

One way to pin this down further is to become aware of messages that you send yourself. These messages are like tapes playing in the back of your mind. They may not originally have been your own messages. They may have come from elsewhere: parents, the media, friends, school. In which case, they are part of your conditioning.

Elaine: I've always had my financial independence by working freelance – right through my marriage. It gives me a great feeling of self esteem and comes from my mother drumming into me 'always stand on your own feet!'

Carla: I always approach my work as a Transport Co-ordinator painstakingly and have to do it that bit better than anyone else around me. I think it comes from everyone in my teens telling me that as a black woman I would have to be ten times as good as anyone else to get anywhere at all.

Here are some head tapes about:

appearance	—	'make sure you always look smart'
older people	—	'your elders are your betters'
men	—	'they enjoy the thrill of the chase'
other women	—	'why don't you behave like Fiona?'
things you do	—	'as long as you come out on top'
things that go wrong	—	'that's the day ruined'
things that go well	—	'it was only luck'
eating	—	'finish it up – think of the starving millions'
attitude	—	'you should be content with what you've got'

What are your head tapes?

Write down at least six of your head tapes, and the effect they have had on your life so far:

1. Is the queen coming to dinner. / DAFT + DEAD + FAILED
2. You're greedy / MAD
3. Your eyes have gone green. you lying MAD
4. How dare you speak back to me – beaten MAD
5. Don't make waves. Scaled + possibly dead
6. Stand on chair with hands on head. ridicule Dead
7. H + H / Dead. Had bad life / Not my prob
8. SFE / You only ridicule those you love
9. You're scruffy. They are scruffy MAD
10. You can't cook, run a home, tidy up – out, Stupid, useless give it here I'll do it. MAD

Summary and action

In this section you have done a lot of work on yourself. This provides you with a launch pad for the more outgoing, practical skills sections later in the Workbook. Know yourself and value yourself so that you can become more fully yourself.

Your personal resource bank

— log the positive advantages of being a woman, being the age and race you are, and having the level of physical ability that you have
— transfer the values that matter the most to you, to keep as a reminder.

Further optional reading

Susan Jeffers – *Feel the Fear and Do It Anyway* – published by Arrow Books
Jenny Morris – *Pride against Prejudice – Transforming attitudes to disability* – published by Womens Press
Angela Mason and Anya Palmer – *Queer Bashing* – published by Stonewall

Action

What are you going to do now to build on the advantages of being you?
What are you going to do to turn the disadvantages into advantages?

Here are some suggestions:

— do something you've never done before
— place yourself in stretching situations
— build your positive attitudes
— consciously stay alert and open to a difficult person
— at the end of every day, identify something new that you've learnt
— take one small step towards meeting one of your values
— associate with people who help you feel positive

I will ___ALWAYS BE THE Best I can be___ by _____

I will _____ by _____

I will _____ by _____

I will _____ by _____

Profile

Sandra Benjamin
Manager, Training Group Quality Assurance, Wellcome Foundation

When I started working in 1965 as a junior laboratory technician my intention was to work there until I was 18 and then begin my training as a nurse – my ambition since the age of seven. After a year I discovered that I liked the work environment in the laboratory and decided not to go into nursing. I did a range of tasks, working in production and quality control and for my first six working years I had no career goals. At 21 I was given a team of my own to manage. I disliked it intensely and left to work in the USA as a counsellor at a summer camp.

Learning point: Knowing what you *don't* want can be as useful as knowing what you want.

I returned to the company to carry out development work with an individual who was both sexist and racist, but at the same time, a very good teacher. Working with this individual, there were many days when I cried with the frustration of not being allowed to do proper laboratory work. I persevered in the area and when I demonstrated I was there to stay, I eventually did most of the work in the area. The manager of the unit noticed this and gave me projects of my own to work on.

Learning point: Do not give up, keep on trying.

In 1973 I had my first son. It was unusual in the organisation to have women returning to work; I had to, because of my need to support my son and myself, and I was keen to keep my first significant promotion. I was only about the third woman on the site to return to work so soon after having a baby. Now there are 30 working mothers out of a workforce of 127, and 70% of our pregnant women return to work within seven months of giving birth. 16 have returned to work following the birth of a second child.

Learning point: Set a new precedent.

I had to promise I would work as late as possible in my pregnancy and return to work as soon as I could. I returned to work when my son was three months old and was put on three months probation because of fears that I might not be able to cope! This probationary period was upsetting, as when returning after my trip to the States this had not happened. I had to work hard on return to work, and was treated more like a male technician because my manager's perception was that I now had to work.

A year later I was asked to manage an area that had always previously been managed by males on a certain grade. I was told that I had to prove my potential before being promoted. I accepted the challenge and set about not only having to cope with male technicians who resented working for a woman, but also with the poor design of the laboratory. The work stations were designed for very tall men and as I am 5'1" I could not teach and work comfortably with lots of the apparatus. I had a platform built for me to reach work stations and people used to come into my laboratory to laugh at me on my platform. I learnt to do a tap dance on my platform and the novelty of me working on it soon disappeared!

Learning point: Being a pioneer makes you very visible. This can be helpful, but can also make life very tough.

In 1975 I got married and I knew when other women in the department had married they were called into the laboratory superintendent's office and asked about their future intentions about starting a family, so I only told the personnel department. In 1977 I was due for a promotion to the highest technical grade. I became pregnant and with promotions only being implemented at certain times of the year I knew that my name would not be put forward if it was known that I was pregnant. Only when it was obvious that my name was not going to be submitted until the autumn did I announce my pregnancy. I took on additional responsibilities and took work home with me to demonstrate that I still wanted a career now that I was a married mother of two.

Learning point: Demonstrate actively that you want a career.

I returned to work after five months following the birth of my second son and took up the same post; life was relatively easy apart from breastfeeding and looking after three people as well as a full day's work. Then I became a volunteer for the probation service and became active in trade union activities. I began to have to balance my work, family, probation clients *and* trade union activities. My husband has always supported me by being around to look after the children; he was always on time when I had to go out. In return I always had his dinner and a good pudding.

I was promoted soon after returning to work and I thought it was all I wanted. I had no other career aspirations. My trade union activities increased when a group of women representatives decided to look at issues around equality of opportunity for women, especially those concerned with child care and maternity benefits. We persuaded the company to bring in an outside consultant to review equality of opportunity and this initiative received a lot of publicity within ASTMS (now MSF), not only because it was one of the first in the private sector, but also because we had only 20% trade union membership. I was regularly asked to speak externally to trade union groups and became better known. I think I was also remembered because I am black and there were very few active black lay representatives at that time.

Learning point: High profile activity, while it may be perceived as negative, can also be beneficial.

By 1983 I knew my job inside out and needed to do something different. My trade union and voluntary work provided me with some useful stimulus, but not enough. For the first time in my working life I did some career planning. I did not have a Ph.D. so I knew that if I stayed in the same area, I would end up reporting to a male, and the thought of being treated as a schoolgirl did not appeal to me. So I applied for administrative jobs where I could use my 18 years laboratory-based experience. At the third attempt I obtained a post in a section dealing with quality control issues of medical and veterinary biological products. This section had no effective mechanism for dealing with QC issues on projects and most managers saw their responsibility as getting registered products out of the door. I identified that there was a gap in our system and went to my boss. Luckily she had also recognised this gap so I did not have much persuading to do.

Learning point: If you notice a gap in the organisation, try and fill it and let everyone know that you have.

It took me 20 months and much frustration to get regraded.

Learning point: Don't give up. Keep your determination going.

In the last seven years I have also worked externally as an equal opportunity trainer. This started as a result of the ex-GLC policy of having black and white trainers working together. My training experience outside has had some benefits in my company.

Five years ago I was asked to do a review of training within my department at work. In the pharmaceutical industry we are required to have training plans, a formal recorded training system which is reviewed and monitored regularly to assess its effectiveness. As a result of my work the post of Training Co-ordinator was created for our Biotech with responsibilities for the on-the-job training needs of 320 production, development, and quality assurance staff. I now combine this post with managing the Development and Licensing Section.

Learning point: Grow your own job. Just because the job you want doesn't exist, it doesn't mean it won't happen.

Two years ago I was at the crossroads of my career, but I had the decision about which direction I should go made for me. My organisation, like many others, made the decision to rationalise and focus on a specific core business. This meant that over 300 people were made redundant, many of them people who had been with the organisation for 25 years. My previous decision to develop transferable skills meant that I was offered a post as the Training Manager for Quality Assurance.

Learning point: Planning so that you can learn and develop transferable skills makes you employable.

It has meant that I now work on a different site. Although it is only 16 miles from the site that I had worked on for 26 years, the culture is completely different. I have found myself having to readjust, establish links and develop new relationships in an environment which is overtly racist. I can, however, focus on developing new skills. I have also been on a steep learning curve, which I think will continue for a long time.

Learning point: In a changing world, learn how to use change positively and to change yourself.

I have a few basic survival rules that work for me at home:

— No shopping for food after 12 o'clock on Saturday afternoons.
— At least an hour of window shopping on Saturday is a must.
— My personal stereo is always in my handbag.
— I have a break at lunch time on Sundays to have a drink and catch up with the gossip with my mother.
— Discuss the football results with the three men in my life during our main meal on Sundays.

Food for thought

Sue Stoessl
Marketing Consultant
At present I am working for a number of clients as a marketing consultant. My office is in my home. This way of life allows me time to pursue some activities outside my paid employment. For instance, I chair a charity called Find Your Feet which sets up projects throughout the third world to help women feed their families and their communities by producing leaf protein from locally grown crops.

You should change jobs even if it is more comfortable or convenient not to. Change is stimulating and necessary to build a career.

Rosemary Raddon
Head of Librarianship and Information Studies – Newcastle-upon-Tyne Polytechnic

The most important thing, looking back, is not to be afraid of change and chance, but be able to link all the changes and chances together. Value the people who have had important effects on you – in my case my research supervisor and my father, but, more than anything else, know yourself – the hardest part but the most important. Decide what is most important to you and then do it – it's your life!

Vikki Worthington
Researcher – Central Independent Television plc

After five years of working in social work, Vikki Worthington knew that it wasn't what she wanted to do for the rest of her working life. A career in television was something she had always fancied. Many women would have dismissed this as an impossible dream, but not Vikki. She set out to make it work. 'I did a part-time course in television production and I joined a film workshop', she says, 'I also worked on hospital radio to build up broadcasting experience.'

Vikki applied for 70 jobs, had eight interviews and was finally offered the position of a researcher on educational programmes with Central Television. 'I knew that if I just turned up as an ex-social worker who wanted to get into television I would be at a disadvantage. But if I was prepared to do my homework, and to add some kind of professional experience, then the fact that I would be up against people ten years younger coming straight from college wouldn't matter so much. I could use my maturity to my advantage.

In fact I ignored the age limit that was given in the advertisement for the job I applied for and got. I think that's a tip well worth remembering.'

WHAT YOU'VE GOT GOING FOR YOU

4

What lies behind us and what lies before us are tiny matters compared to what lies within us.

Ralph Waldo Emerson

Objective: To put everything you've got going for you into action

This section is important because:

— you need to assess where you shine and where you need polish
— knowing where your strength lies helps you take the next step
— valuing yourself gives you the confidence to tackle things

Contents:

— your achievements
— positive and negative forces
— qualities and strengths
— your skills audit
— your qualifications
— your assertiveness audit
— confidence
— summary and action
— profile of Barbara Stephens

What you've got going for you

You have so many aspects of yourself that you could use to achieve your goals. Don't underestimate them, put them to work for you.

Your achievements

Wherever you are on life's path, you have behind you all your achievements and your failures too. You have before you your unfulfilled dreams and ambitions.

What achievements in your life are you really proud of? Write at least six. Include any areas of your life – family, work, home, social, sports, hobbies, relationships, community activities, old achievements as well as recent ones.

1

2

3

4

5

6

7

8

9

10

What is there that you haven't achieved that you may still want to try to achieve? Don't worry at this point about whether they seem achievable or not.

1

2

3

4

5

6

7

8

9

10

We'll come back to these later.

Positive and negative forces

If you imagine your life as a journey, then what are the forces that are helping you move forward, making it worthwhile and preventing you from being stuck?

Susan: My divorce has gone through and I'm in control of my own life again. I need a challenge – I feel under-used. I'm not afraid to try new things, perhaps a change in the type of work I'm doing. I'm keen to make new changes. I've got two very supportive friends. There's got to be more to life than this!

List all the forces helping you here; everything inside you and outside you. Write down absolutely everything you can think of and ask family, friends or colleagues what they think and add their suggestions even when you don't fully agree with them:

What's holding you back?

Across your path there will be hurdles – they hold you back, deflect you, slow you down, and may even stop you. Getting over them will take some effort on your part.

Lai Chan: Not being brave enough to climb out of my comfortable rut. Don't want to upset my partner. Afraid of seeming selfish. I hate interviews. Men dominate engineering. Fear of making a fool of myself.

List all the things that are standing in your way, internal and external, and if you can visualise them, draw pictures of how they appear to you:

Taking control

The exciting and encouraging aspect of this analysis is to realise how much you can influence the hurdles that you've written down. There are very few that are impervious to change. So few that we can identify them here:

— you can do little to change your sex
— you cannot change your race
— you cannot change your age

But you can change your ATTITUDE to these, and your ways of dealing with the prejudice in others.

You have limited possibilities of transforming:

— society generally
— your company/organisation
— your level of disability

But you can change your ATTITUDE to these, by updating your information about them, and being alert to changes.

YOU HAVE THE ABILITY TO CHANGE EVERYTHING ELSE – IF YOU WANT TO

Write down things that you want to change about your attitude to yourself:

I'd like to be less hard on myself. I want to believe I'm worthwhile.

Qualities and strengths

Knowing your qualities and strengths helps you:

— be confident
— choose appropriate goals
— know when you can achieve goals
— see which situations you will handle well

List your strengths – the things about you that you feel are positive, the qualities you have – in the top left-hand box. Fill it right up, and be as specific as you can.

If your mind has gone a complete blank, talk to your partner, friends, boss and colleagues to get their ideas on what your strengths are.

Now do the same with your weaknesses in the bottom right-hand box.

YOUR STRENGTHS

flexible

YOUR WEAKNESSES

impatient

Strengths and weaknesses are a balancing act

There are no such things as weaknesses, only qualities that are out of balance.

A quality becomes a strength when it is right for you and the situation.
A quality becomes a weakness when it is either overdone or underdone for you and the situation.

For example: Being flexible is a strength. If you overdo being flexible, you become aimless, which could become a weakness. If you underdo being flexible, you become rigid in your thinking, which could also become a weakness. Being impatient is a weakness, but underlying it is a great quality – your energy and enthusiasm to get on with things. It's just gone too far one way!

Go back to your chart on page 69 and in the bottom left-hand corner write down the potential strength that you have in your out-of-balance 'weaknesses'.
Here are some suggestions to help you:

UNDERDONE ←	QUALITY →	OVERDONE
unreliable	reliable	become indispensable
disrespectful	respectful of others	deferential
slow	quick to act	rash
pessimistic	optimistic	impractical/unrealistic
closed mind	open-minded	vague
spineless	determined	ruthless
rigid thinking	being flexible	aimless
uninterested	interested	nosey
unambitious	ambitious	ruthless
disorganised	organised	bossy
timid	courageous	foolhardy
timorous	confident	arrogant

Once you have found the potential strength that is being underdone or overdone you will be able to see what kind of action you could take. For example, if you suspect your interest in people overdoes itself to become nosiness, then observe yourself and stop yourself asking extra questions to satisfy your curiosity.

If you see that your lack of confidence means you appear timorous, find small things with which to push yourself a bit further than you would normally go.

When you've looked at your weaknesses, look back again at your strengths just to check you are not in danger of overdoing them.

Ask someone who knows you well how they see you. Often it is easier for other people to see your strengths than it is for you to see your own, but remember other people's views are just their opinions. They may not have it right – get a second opinion on any doubtful ones.

Your skills audit

A skill is an ability to do something. You will feel more confident when you are doing things you are already skilled at.

Don't forget or play down the many skills you have acquired because you don't do them perfectly! You can assess the level of your ability to do anything, or you can decide that you simply have a gap. A gap doesn't mean you have no ability to do something, it simply means that you haven't had the opportunity to discover your ability.

When you use your skills in the right order, it usually means you do things better. For example, rushing into something, and then afterwards thinking of a plan, is probably not the most effective approach! It is usually called having the benefit of hindsight!

Getting things in the right order means using your skills like this:

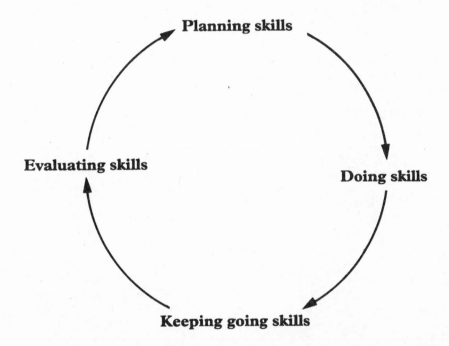

The logical starting point in the cycle is at planning skills but very often it is our evaluating skills which push us into wanting to do something different or differently.

> The next pages have lists of skills for which you are asked to rate yourself. Of course, this will be your subjective rating, so before you start, photocopy these pages twice, and ask your manager/work contact and/or a close friend to rate you too. This gives you a comparison and some useful feedback.

The gaps at the bottom of each category are for you to add any other skills that you want to, such as technical skills that are specific to your work.

Rate yourself 1 – 5 as follows:

5 — extremely good at this
4 — good at this
3 — OK at this
2 — not too good at this
1 — terrible at this

Planning skills

Planning skills are about the future.

Having good planning skills minimises risks and gives a structure to whatever you want to make happen. They enable you to consider possibilities and make decisions. They use your creative and pragmatic qualities. Add your own ideas to the end of the list.

gathering information ☐

using my imagination ☐

visualising what might happen ☐

having ideas ☐

organising ideas ☐

diagnosing ☐

categorising ☐

predicting accurately ☐

estimating ☐

budgeting ☐

setting objectives ☐

anticipating ☐

making decisions ☐

exploring and expanding ideas ☐

assessing ☐

interpreting information ☐

☐

☐

☐

☐

☐

Doing skills

Doing skills are about the present. Having made the plan, doing skills enable you to carry it out. They fall into three categories – doing things in relation to yourself, other people, and things.

Doing skills enable you to get things started and moving.

using physical strength ☐	decision making ☐
using dexterity ☐	changing plans ☐
using co-ordination ☐	taking risks ☐
motivating others ☐	understanding instructions ☐
persuading others ☐	giving instructions ☐
initiating ☐	following instructions ☐
enthusing ☐	attending to detail ☐
reading ☐	prioritising ☐
writing ☐	using time ☐
speaking ☐	negotiating ☐
calculating ☐	expressing feelings ☐
observing ☐	pacing ☐
using visual awareness ☐	seeing steps to be taken ☐
operating machinery ☐	organising resources ☐

add relevant technical
skills here:

using laboratory equipment ☐   ☐

technical drawing ☐   ☐

☐   ☐

☐   ☐

☐   ☐

☐   ☐

Keeping-going skills

Keeping-going skills enable you to sustain action, and also enable you to enjoy things.

knowing when to stop	☐	helping	☐
knowing when to keep going	☐	using your intuition	☐
encouraging yourself	☐	having fun	☐
encouraging others	☐	speeding up	☐
laughing	☐	slowing down	☐
creating – words, music, etc.	☐	changing plans	☐
listening	☐	finishing things	☐
counselling	☐	attending to detail	☐
coaching	☐	dealing with conflict	☐

Evaluating skills

Evaluating skills are about getting the best from the past. They enable you to learn, make decisions and make better plans next time.

assessing objectively	☐	seeing the bigger picture	☐
measuring results	☐	drawing conclusions	☐
comparing results	☐	reviewing	☐
observing objectively	☐	adapting	☐
letting go	☐	decision making	☐
	☐		☐
	☐		☐
	☐		☐

What does it mean?

Got more going for you than you thought? Got less going for you than you thought?

Check that your modesty isn't preventing you boasting a bit or that the perfectionist in you isn't stopping you being satisfied with something that is less than perfect.

How does your own rating compare with that of your manager and/or friend? Do they see you differently?

Use their rating to challenge your own as they may see you more clearly than you see yourself. Who's got it right?

Use this space for your notes of things you've learnt from this exercise:

Transferable skills

The use of skills is severely limited by putting technical or professional labels on them which lock them into a particular profession. Assessing them under broader headings gives you more flexibility to transfer them to another form of work.

For example: A good secretary can be described as 'just a secretary' or as being very skilled at:

understanding instructions	getting on with people
making decisions	interpreting information
using dexterity	persuading others
using co-ordination	pacing
operating machinery	breaking things down
using visual awareness	organising resources
using time	organising people
attention to detail	assessing
working to deadlines	encouraging yourself
negotiating	encouraging others

Transferring your skills

Women, particularly those who've had a career break or who are unemployed, need to recognise their own skills and help potential new employers recognise just how transferable some skills are.

For example:
A bank clerk may wish to become a Marketing Assistant.
An unemployed mother may want to be a Store Manager.
A woman on the production line may aim for an Area Sales Representative's job.

Eva: I left school at 16, trained as a secretary, worked for a year or two then studied at night school to go to university. Then my itchy feet took me to France and Portugal to work. When I came back to England, I trained to teach English as a foreign language and so embarked on a new career at 40. I had to persuade people that my skills in learning and working in other languages were transferable to helping others do the same. My elderly mother needed me at home, so I had to give up teaching. After she died, I began again, at 50. My skills in being organised as a teacher coupled with my abilities in helping other people got me a job in the local technical college as assistant librarian. I realised I needed to pick up new specific technical skills and so became computer-literate at 50.
I now run a children's library and have transferred my speaking, persuading others, nurturing others, and coaching skills to encouraging, instructing and entertaining groups of children (not to mention parents and teachers) in the wonderful world of books. I'm coming up to retirement soon and plan to transfer my skills now into yet another wide range of activities.

Write down one aspect of what you do now in your work or current role. Then write alongside the transferable skills it gives you.

— *organising family holidays*

— *gathering information*

— *planning*

— *time management*

— *decision making*

— *budgeting*

LOOK AT YOUR SKILLS IN A TRANSFERABLE WAY – DON'T LIMIT YOURSELF

Your qualifications

Qualifications are rather like theatre tickets. You have to have them to get you through the door, but once through the door everyone else has a similar ticket. They can also be a double-edged sword, with people regarding you as over-qualified, so either way, qualifications are a powerful message.

Qualifications
— can open doors
— can make it difficult to open doors
— give you credibility
— come in all shapes and sizes
— tell people what you have learnt
— tell people what you can do
— tell people what sort of person you are
— can be an asset or a hindrance
— may be helpful or unhelpful
— educational qualifications diminish in value as you get older
— professional qualifications are often highly valued
— people have got to the top without qualifications

Turn to page 246 and log your qualifications under the headings.

If you have qualifications – be proud of your achievements. If you're thinking you haven't got much written down, don't give up but think about what you may need. Some women have got to the top without formal qualifications, but employers are increasingly looking for qualifications.

The qualifications you had when you left school may have opened some doors. By the time you get to your mid-20s, school leaving qualifications are no longer relevant: people are looking for more. Similarly, a degree may not mean so much in your 30s as it did in your 20s. You may need to take more qualifications to suit what you now want to do.

Ways of gaining qualifications
Think about the many ways you can gain qualifications before making future decisions. Award-giving bodies are constantly increasing their flexibility. There are:

— full-time, flexi-time, part-time, block release and short courses
— distance learning, correspondence and Open University-style courses needing little or no time away from home
— evening, day and weekend courses
— fixed schedules and 'take as long as you like' programmes

Which qualifications?
You don't need any formal qualifications at all to start an Open University degree course. Even if, on the other hand, you have a Ph.D. you may still need a vocational qualification to achieve your next goal. Think about the wide range of qualifications before deciding which one to investigate further.

Vocational qualifications

For example: Heavy Goods Vehicle Licence
Public Service Vehicle Licence
City and Guilds Trade and Supervisory Qualifications
Certificates in Management

Academic qualifications

For example: GCSEs
BTEC Certificates and Diplomas for technician and business
qualifications
Degrees — Bachelors — BA
— Masters — MBA
— Doctorate — PhD

Post Graduate and Professional qualifications

For example: State Registered Nurse
Membership of Institute of Mechanical Engineers
Membership of Chartered Institute of Marketing
Membership of the Chartered Institute of Bankers

There are hundreds of other qualifications to choose from.

What qualifications do you want or need to get for your work?

What qualifications do you want to get for your own fun or satisfaction?

Will anyone give you any form of help in getting these qualifications? Your
organisation may have a policy to support the gaining of qualifications that are
directly related to your work.

Find out if you qualify for support. If you don't know, ask your Personnel
Manager or the person who deals with this in your organisation. If you are not
working, or there is no support from your organisation, check other available
sources of sponsorship from charitable trusts or even charitable friends!

Your assertiveness audit

Assertiveness is such an important interpersonal skill that we have devoted two sections of this Workbook to it, so you'll be getting a good dose of it later on! Meanwhile, fill in this questionnaire to assess your current level of assertiveness.

Circle the a, b, c or d response to identify how you tend to behave in these situations. Complete the questionnaire quickly. Your first answers are usually the best and most accurate.

1. You would prefer to have Christmas on your own with your partner/friend; your partner wants to go to his/her family. Do you:

   a)   imply that it's unfair and hope things will change

   b)   go to the family – anything for peace!

   c)   say how you feel and what you would like

   d)   flatly refuse to go

2. You have just started to eat your main course in a restaurant. It should be hot but it's cold. Do you:

   a)   tell the waiter this isn't the item you ordered and order another dish

   b)   carry on and eat it

   c)   tell the waiter it's cold and ask for a fresh hot portion

   d)   point out that this isn't good enough and demand better

3. When a friend or colleague borrows your calculator regularly and forgets to return it to you, do you:

   a)   drop hints at regular intervals

   b)   let it go

   c)   explain the effect on you and ask for it back

   d)   get angry and demand it back

4. An interview panel member asks a question that seems sexist to you, do you:

   a)   quip back a quick retort

   b)   answer as best you can

   c)   express some concern about the question only if you feel OK about it

   d)   point out how wrong it is to ask such questions and refuse to answer

5. When you are entering the car park and are about to reverse into a parking space another driver nips in and pinches the space. Do you:

    a)   block the other car in

    b)   ignore it and find another space

    c)   tell the other driver how annoyed you are and ask him/her to move

    d)   give the other driver a piece of your mind for his/her rudeness

6. When someone criticises your appearance do you:

    a)   say something like 'Well it's my most expensive outfit'

    b)   blush and say nothing

    c)   check what is specifically being said and judge for yourself

    d)   tell him/her it's none of his/her business

7. You are asked to work late for the third time this week. You already have another appointment. Do you:

    a)   give what you think is a cast-iron reason for not staying

    b)   try saying 'no' and end up staying

    c)   say 'no' firmly and say when you have to leave for your other appointment

    d)   complain that it's the third time this week and say a definite 'no'

8. Your family don't seem to be listening when you try telling them about your plans for Saturday. Do you:

    a)   say something like 'Well if anyone's interested I'm...'

    b)   keep quiet

    c)   say how you feel and that it's important to you to tell them about your plans

    d)   talk more loudly

9. When you keep quiet in a situation, is it because:

    a)   you know the silence will have an effect

    b)   you are too upset or frightened to speak

    c)   you have nothing to say

    d)   you're sulking

10. When you feel angry or upset, do you:

   a)   let people know in a roundabout way

   b)   keep quiet

   c)   try to say how you feel and be specific

   d)   explode

Count up how many a's, b's, c's and d's you've scored:

   a [ ]   b [ ]   c [ ]   d [ ]

Mostly b's —   your behaviour tends to be passive

Mostly c's —   this shows that you tend to be assertive, but check that you
                              actually do the things you say you do. Sometimes it is easy
                              to see what the best solution is on paper but a more passive
                              or more aggressive response may slip out in the heat of the
                              moment

Mostly a's and d's —   your behaviour tends to be aggressive. The d's are directly
                              aggressive, whilst the a's are indirectly aggressive and
                              manipulative. Most people confuse assertive behaviour with
                              aggressive behaviour, so it's not unusual to have a high score
                              here

What do you want to change about this pattern?

Confidence

The final part of this section is about confidence.

You may have discovered that, while you've got some things going for you, you lack the self-confidence to stick your neck out and get on with it. Or you may feel you haven't the qualities and qualifications, and need the confidence to so something about it.

You may feel confident in work situations and un-confident in social situations, or the other way round. Everyone's different.

Confidence means:

— being able to start things feeling that you will do reasonably well

— you get on with what you want to do

— you feel that whatever happens, you will be OK inside

Lack of confidence means:

— you feel you can't do things

— you put off doing things till you feel more confident

— you have difficulty doing things

— you feel powerless or uncomfortable, or both

— you feel that whatever you do it won't be good enough

— even when you're doing things well, you feel a bit of an imposter

— you don't even try

Over-confidence means:

— you don't know your own limitations

— you undertake to do things you can't necessarily fulfil

— you are unrealistic

It may be that your reason for working through this book is to help build up your self-confidence. Knowing the situations and people who undermine your self-confidence may give you a clue to the goals you want to set yourself later on in this Workbook.

For example: If you are easily intimidated by more senior people you may want to learn assertiveness skills. If you lack confidence in situations when you're asked to speak in public, consider getting on a course about public speaking, or volunteer to do a very short bit of speaking such as making an announcement at a meeting or giving a vote of thanks to a speaker.

Identify your own confidence peaks and troughs here:

When do you feel most confident?

When I know what I'm doing

Who are the people who help you feel more confident?

When I'm with my friend Clare, I could conquer the world

When do you lack confidence?

When I hear footsteps behind me at night

Who are the people who contribute to your lack of confidence?

When David comes into the room, I immediately feel a fool

Use the situations and people who help your confidence as the foundation stones on which to build further confidence. When your confidence takes a knock, remember these situations and use your supporters.

Summary and action

In this section, you've looked at many of the things that you've got going for you. Look at all the audits positively and enthusiastically and celebrate all the good things you've got to help you reach your goals. In areas where you are disappointed or deflated, decide firstly whether it matters or not – nobody has everything – and if it does matter, then decide what first step you're going to take to do something about it.

Your personal resource bank

This section contributes a major section of your personal resource bank.

Transfer – your achievements from page 66
your strengths from page 69
your best skills from pages 72–74

Further optional reading

Susan Jeffers – *End the Struggle and Dance with Life* – published by Hodder and Stoughton
Louise Hay – *The Power is Within You* – published by Eden Grove
Petruska Clarkson – *The Achilles Syndrome* – published by Element

Action

What action are you now going to take to develop your skills, strengths, qualifications, and confidence?

Here are some suggestions:

— find out about the Open University courses
— polish up my listening skills
— ask my boss to explain his/her ratings of my skills
— volunteer to help out in order to learn about another department/organisation
— get my HGV licence

I will _____ by _____

I will _____ by _____

I will _____ by _____

I will _____ by _____

Profile

Barbara Stephens
Director of Operations, West Cumbria Development Agency

It is just over twenty years since I left school and embarked on my career. I can't help contrasting what I vaguely thought my life would be with what it has turned out to be. I shocked my school by turning down a place at university in order to follow an engineering apprenticeship. This was not because I wanted to blaze any feminist trails; far from it – I just thought engineering sounded more interesting.

I qualified, and became a Production Engineer, and saw my career leading me to becoming a senior engineer. Two things gradually dawned on me: British industry was not ready in the early 1970s for a female Chief Production Engineer, so in that direction lay frustration and I was pretty sure I could do my manager's job better than he could.

There I might have stayed, becoming increasingly frustrated, had it not been for two mentors. The first was a very senior male Production Engineer who had been interested in me, in a grandfatherly fashion, since I joined the company, and the other was a very distinguished woman engineer who had also met me as an apprentice and encouraged me. Both have acted as references at crucial points of my career and at various times their impartial advice has been invaluable.

Learning point: Experienced, impartial, and interested mentors, who give advice and act as references are worth their weight in gold – keep your eyes open for one!

So I stopped being a Production Engineer, and became a management trainee, studying part-time for a Diploma in Management Studies, and for three years everything went swimmingly. Then I was promoted into a position where the problems were so great they needed a magician, not a very green and junior manager. I was too inexperienced to recognise that I was totally out of my depth, and the job lasted only eight months before the situation came to a head and it was plain that I was unable to continue.

I was devastated, but the company recognised that they had been partially at fault, and moved me sideways into a sales and marketing job, something I had never expected to do as a job. I surprised myself by being very successful.

Learning point: Very few people get through their career without failure. Put it behind you, try and learn from it, and don't think it will blight your life from now on.

The sales and marketing job lasted for five years, and I think I would have been happily continuing with the same job now, but company policy and circumstances changed, and the job became less satisfying. I found a new job in project engineering – a useful next step in my career.

In my 15-year career up to that point, I was active as a speaker, encouraging girls to consider engineering as a career, working with the Women's Engineering Society, and becoming a school governor. I was, to my surprise, asked to apply for a conference in Australia as a future 'leader of tomorrow's society'. This was not how I saw myself! Working on the basis that if I was turned down I wouldn't be any worse off, I applied and was accepted!

Learning point: Always seize an opportunity, however unlikely you think it is that you will succeed. Even if you don't succeed, you're not any further back than you were before you started.

The conference will always be one of the outstanding experiences of my life, not just because it was a challenging and unique experience, but because I returned convinced that I had yet to fulfil my potential, and confident enough to do something about it! At the same time, the company I had always been with was hitting bad times, so I started looking around for jobs outside.

One job in particular appealed to me. The only problem was that it asked for a graduate, and I was an ex-apprentice. I was pretty certain that I could do the job, and put a lot of effort into the application, in particular citing work I had done with committees, which I thought was relevant to the job as described. I also fielded the best references I could think of. I thought I had little chance of success, and once again, I succeeded against my expectations. My boss tells me that my experience in other fields contributed to my being selected.

Learning point: Experience is transferable. Don't be afraid to cite something you have done in one area of your life in order to achieve something in another area.

In my late thirties I was doing a much more responsible job than I had ever envisaged. My company considered me under-qualified, and sponsored me on a part time Master of Business Administration degree. Everything was going swimmingly.

In 1990, halfway through my Master's in Business Administration course, I had a major road accident which left me partially disabled. In 1992, just as I was completing the MBA and mastering working as a disabled person, the office closed and I was made redundant. Who would want a 40-something female engineer who couldn't walk far?

With support from numerous friends, colleagues, family and husband – and after 264 job applications, I now have a superb job, fulfilling a worthwhile task, which I won in competition with 180 able-bodied males. And suddenly, life is good again!

Learning point: When life hands you lemons – find ways of making lemonade! Grit your teeth and keep going – there is something at the other end.

FINDING SUPPORT

5

A brain to pick, a shoulder to cry on, and a kick in the pants.

Natasha Josefowitz, *Paths To Power*

Objective: To identify the effects that other people have on you
To activate support

This section is important because:

— you can build on other people's support
— only a very few of us make it on our own
— you can help other people to help you
— people can make your life hellish or heavenly!

Contents:

— how people influence you
— the roles people play
— networking
— building your contacts
— summary and action
— profile of Marion Way

Finding support

None of us live in a vacuum. You may be all too well aware of the influence other people have had on you, or you may feel that you've done it all on your own. Being aware of the effect of other people on you can help you find support.

How people influence you

The influence that other people have can vary enormously:

— directly or indirectly
— negatively or positively
— consciously or unconsciously

Influences that appeared negative at the time, in retrospect, can prove positive:

Being determined to make a success of my career was the only way I knew of delaying the marriage I knew my parents wanted for me.

Going back to work because of a divorce, and re-discovering a career that I really love.

Making a go of flat-sharing, because my mother was so set against it.

Go back to page 49 and review your life events. Think of them in terms of people, and the influences they've had.

Write down a list of the key people who have affected you and how they have influenced you. Most people have a mixture of family, friends, work colleagues, bosses, teachers, and passing acquaintances.

First boss — boosted my confidence, had faith in my ability to handle the job.

Help and hindrance

It is very useful to identify where the help and hindrance came from in the past.

Look at your list on the previous page and answer these questions:

— Where are the positive and conscious sources of help and support in the past?

Everywhere people have got to know me.   Never at home

— Which of those people will continue to help and support you now?

All of them

— Is your support coming from home or work, or a mix of both?

Work, friends, family

— What additional sources of help and support do you want to build up?

A bit more learning – but its all there

— Which people have held you back?

Perhaps fortunately you don't know about these people – till later but its interesting to watch them when you do find out.

— How might they continue to hold you back?

I won't give them the opportunity or permission

— Is there any pattern or theme emerging from your past influences? It doesn't matter if there isn't but it's helpful to realise if there is! For example: sarcastic remarks from friends and colleagues have often stopped you doing things.

I didn't realise how well liked I was. I am now happy. I don't have to act the fool

Active goodwill

If you can think of everyone you are acquainted with (and research shows that we all can know about 500 people) they are likely to fall roughly into three categories along a scale of 'helpfulness'.

— 10% are people who will actively help you – no matter what

— 80% are people who aren't particularly interested in you, but would help, if you took the initiative

— 10% are people who don't like you, or what you stand for, and will actively hold you back or try to stop you

You don't need to worry about the 10% made up of your supporters – they like you and will actively support you, give you ideas and contacts, and encourage you. Don't forget about them.

There's no point in worrying about the other 10% – you won't win everyone over, so it may be a waste of time and energy trying to turn these people round.

The huge majority of people you know will be in the 80% in the middle. These people can be described as having 'latent goodwill' towards you. They do not lie awake at night worrying about you, but equally are not going to slip banana skins under your feet. They probably don't think about you at all! These people are important to you – it is your job to turn their latent goodwill into active goodwill. You'll have to take the initiative here.

Marjorie: An old school friend used to work in a bank before she took a career break. I'm thinking of setting up my own business and therefore I would need a small loan. So I decided to pick her brains about how to go about it. She was very helpful, gave me lots of tips on preparing my case and helped me to realise that an overdraft facility might be appropriate. I feel when I go to see the bank manager I'll be better able to talk 'bank language'.

As you go through the rest of this section, consider the potential of the people you know, as well as their present role.

IT'S UP TO YOU TO TAKE THE FIRST STEP, TO KNOW WHICH BATTLES TO FIGHT, AND WHICH TO LEAVE ALONE.

The roles people play

The next exercise is to help you identify the differing ways in which people influence you at present, and to identify the gaps which will give clues for action in the future.

This is difficult to do, because relationships do not fall into such clear cut categories. Our lives are much more complicated and subjective than that. However, one major contributory factor in any form of development is in our relationships. A useful way of looking at people is in terms of the role they play in our lives, while remembering that one person may play several roles – often all at once!

Hundreds of women on other programmes have identified these 10 roles.

Write the names of people you know under each category and make a few notes about why they are there:

1 Energy givers — people who give you warmth

We all need these people – they give you the warmth and reassurance to keep going when life gets tough, and give comfort when you fail. Their warmth restores you. They are easy to be with. They boost your confidence because you know they are on your side. ⊐

---

2 Energy drainers — people who drain your energy

These people don't realise the effect they have on you, but being with them either makes you feel ineffective and frustrated, or exhausted and apathetic. They may be very nice, well meaning people, but they take away your energy to achieve your goals. They may be overbright and chatty or dull and gloomy. They take up too much of your time and sap your confidence. ℞

---

3 Role models — people who have set the precedent

These are the people who have done what you are thinking of doing and against whom you may be compared. They can be a positive influence, such as opening up new areas for women in the world of work, or negative, such as setting standards of behaviour which you don't value.

Grandma Moses, Col Saunders, Helen

4 Heroes and heroines – people who inspire you

These may be people you know personally and could also be people who you don't know. They can be alive or dead, real or fictitious. They contribute to your sense of purpose and your determination, and can help you see where your goals for the future lie or inspire ideas of what you may do or become.

BSTA

5 Gatekeepers – people who control your access to opportunities

These people control your access to training, information, resources, people, support, and ideas, and they mostly like to have recognition for doing this. It may be their job to do so – Personnel Managers fall into this category. Family and friends open and shut doors too. Gatekeepers can be helpful or unhelpful and can be more senior or more junior than you.

T

6 Neutral people — those who will help if you ask them

These are the people who aren't particularly interested in you, but will help if you take the initiative. You will have to ask for their advice, ideas and information, but they will be quite happy to give it. This is likely to be a large category and may overlap with many of the others. They are not telepathic so you will need to tell them what you want.

WORK

7 Enemies — people who actively oppose your progress

These people don't like you, or what you stand for. They may resent your success or feel threatened by what you're trying to do. You may not have anyone opposing you quite so strongly as this implies but you may know of people on the edge of this role. Enemies put you down, undermine the support you get from others and the confidence you build up. They may be acting on a prejudice.

8 Mentors — people who believe in you more than you believe in yourself

Mentors support you, give you advice, give you a kick, understand your work, and believe in your potential. Anyone can be a mentor, but ex-bosses and colleagues often seem to fill this role. It is important that they can see you objectively, and give you constructive feedback.

9 Gardener bosses — people who grow you

These are the bosses who have a reputation for giving people opportunities and for stretching them. After that — it's up to you! If you grab the opportunities offered by these bosses, you can develop more quickly. If you haven't come across one of these, keep your eyes and ears open! Gardener bosses are good at delegation and training and enjoy seeing others do well.

10 Apprentices — people to whom you are especially helpful and encouraging

Who are you opening doors for? These people will be the special few who you are helping up behind you. They look to you for encouragement and may regard you as a mentor, or as in any one of categories 1, 2, 3, 4 or 5. These people are important because you need to free yourself up to develop, so growing your own successor at work is a key activity, as well as helping people outside work.

How does this help?

To get the best out of the previous exercise, answer these questions:

— Are there any categories predominating? If so, which?

— How do you feel about this?

— Are there any categories totally missing? If so, which?

— Do you want to do anything about this?

— Are you inspired?

— Where is your main help and support coming from?
    my own initiatives

— Who is giving you constructive feedback?
    myself

— Do you want to alter or expand this?

— Is the path ahead helped or hindered by the precedent that's been set?

— Are you getting enough objective advice and feedback? *No*

— Are you being challenged enough?

— Are you getting enough warmth? *No*

— Is your access to information and ideas wide enough, or are all your ideas coming from one area?

— What do you want to change?

Flossie

Further optional work: To take this further, you can look at this exercise back to front and look at the roles that you play in other people's lives. Are you being cast in the same role too often? Do you want to change the balance of the roles you're in?

Networking

The word 'Network' can have positive or negative overtones, or it can have a specific technical meaning as it does in computing. Here we are using it to mean a positive process of mutual support.

The old boy network is probably the most well known example, and has manipulative and negative undertones. However, the practice of extending your contacts to give you greater access to ideas, people, support and opportunities is extremely positive and influential.

Your own network is simply everyone you know. If you extend that again to everyone that they know, your network multiplies many times again.

Most of us get to know other people in two ways.

— haphazardly – people that you know just for their own sake
— through association – people that you know through a mutual association of ideas and/or interests

For example: family
neighbours
other parents
people you know through your children
people you know through your school/college
hobby interest groups
people you meet on holiday
members of women's groups
people in your workplace
fellow professionals
people in other organisations
members of professional institutes
people in the UK
people on courses
people with similar interests worldwide

Add your own categories:

The more people you know, the greater your flexibility to achieve your goals. You do not have to become friends with everyone, indeed you may not even like them. Knowing people is rather like travel – it broadens the mind!

Think about who your contacts are at the moment

— Are they up-to-date contacts, or go back a long way? A bit of both?

— Are they work people?

— Are there enough 'outside work' people for you?

— Are they spread around all the departments at work?

— Are you networking with people away from work?

— When do you meet people who are totally different from you?

— In which areas do you want to build up your contacts?

— Do you have a contact who can help you do that?

— Are you adding new contacts to your list?

— What do you do to keep in contact with all these people? See them, send them a Christmas card, phone them regularly?

— Are you tending to network with all the same sort of people?

— Which people do you need to/want to make contact with?

DON'T UNDERESTIMATE PEOPLE — THEY MOSTLY WANT TO HELP

Building your contacts

Informal networks

Most women have a network of other people around them – family, friends, neighbours, acquaintances, work colleagues, members of clubs or societies, women who do the same hobbies or sports.

Use the opportunity of the time spent with this Workbook to widen your personal network and get to know as many people as possible.

Get in touch with two other women that you are acquainted with, who are working in areas or departments, or have special interests, that you know very little about.

Find out   —   what they do

         —   how they feel about what they do

         —   how they could help you

         —   how you could help them

         —   anything else!

Formal networks

In addition to getting to know people informally, there are hundreds of more formal networks, ranging from Parent Teacher Associations, through to professional institutes and women's groups.

There are also increasing numbers of networks in organisations; some quite informal and not registered anywhere, so you will have to do some detective work to find them. Others have formed after a training course. Some large organisations have formal networks, such as Women in BP, Women in ICL, and in some cases, networks relate to a whole industry or area, such as Women in Publishing, Women in Banking, Women in the North West. The Appendix gives the head office address of some of the national ones, but you'll need to enquire to find out about local branches and meetings.

In the Appendix at the back of this Workbook are addresses of some of the more prominent women's networks. This is just the tip of the iceberg, and if you do some detective work, you will find many more. If there isn't a branch in your area, start one! Most of these groups were started by one or two women getting together casually, and building it up from there.

Contact one external group to find out about them and find out what internal groups there are in your department/area.

Summary and action

In this section, you've taken a brief look at the role and influence of other people in your life, and how you can build on that positively. You have already been networking but you may want to do this more consciously in the future.

Your personal resource bank

Keep a note of the really positive people in the present, and the people who are of potential help for the future.

Note down any information about networks that you've discovered.

Further optional reading

Lily Segerman-Peck – *Networking and Mentoring* – published by Piatkus

Action

What action will you take now to help people to help you?

Here are some suggestions:

— ask someone I admire about their career path
— revive an old contact
— ask my boss for straight feedback
— talk to someone in a different department about what they do there
— get an information pack from the Women in Management network
— let go of a redundant relationship

I will _____ by _____

I will _____ by _____

I will _____ by _____

I will _____ by _____

Profile

Marion Way
Ambulance Person, London Ambulance Service and Deputy Leader of London Borough of Hillingdon

I left school at the age of 15 with no qualifications, and became a shop assistant. I very quickly realised it was a dead end job, went back to college with the aim of becoming a nurse, and joined as a cadet nurse at the age of 17.

I left nursing when I got married at the age of 19 and had a job with a pharmaceutical company. This is where I experienced sexual harassment for the first time, although I didn't recognise it for some considerable time. Rather than tackling it, I left the company, mainly because I didn't know how to! Knowing how and who and where to go wasn't apparent until I joined a Trade Union.

Meanwhile, I had two daughters and became divorced after 11 years of marriage.

Learning point: You can survive and support yourself by being positive, recognising why relationships fail and looking forward positively, rather than backwards with regret.

I got married for the second time in 1978 and had a third daughter. At this stage, life became negative for a time until a friend suggested youth work as a way of making my life more meaningful. The idea appealed to me, so I researched courses available and contacted local authorities to discover what was involved. As a result, I became a Youth and Community worker working with girls under 16, mothers with young babies, and senior citizens.

Learning point: Do your homework.

I originally became interested in Trade Unions and Politics mainly because of funding reductions in the Youth Service which made me very angry, and I resolved to do something about it.

Learning point: Identify the issues about which you feel strongly – they can give you the energy for the next step.

I joined the Ambulance Service in 1986 as a day worker, non emergency. I really wanted to do Accident and Emergency work but because of shift work and childcare problems it wasn't possible. It was then I realised why there were very few women on Accident and Emergency. I did a lot more research, and also became the Trade Union representative for the station.

At this time the Trade Union had a very negative reputation and lacked credibility with the staff. Both the Service and the Trade Union were dominated by men with very macho outlooks and attitudes. The ambulance dispute in 1989 really gave me the opportunity to come to the forefront, both at work and in the Trade Union. It tested all my organising skills and experience of dealing with people that I had gained from the Youth and Community work. I spoke at meetings for the first time and gained the confidence to speak publicly in a hostile environment.

I had used every opportunity to go on courses both through the Trade Union and the Labour Party: Confidence Building, Public Speaking, Negotiating Skills, etc. I also lobbied for more courses specifically aimed at women. From all of this, life really took off, setting me on the continuing path of a satisfying challenging career outside work and home.

Learning point: Don't just look for opportunities to grow, learn and develop inside work. Outside activities can also give you valuable skills and confidence to help you along the way.

Along the way, I became President and Vice President of the constituency party, Local Councillor, School Governor, member of the Community Health Council, Deputy Leader of the Council, Chair of Social Services, the first woman Convenor for the Ambulance Service and the first woman Chair of the Central Staff Committee.

Learning point: It is never too late – all this I achieved after the age of 40. Always try to be positive, constructive, and recognise that change is something constant in life and work with it rather than against.

Say yes to something new and remember that the trying is the important thing and not necessarily the success.

If I have been the token woman on occasions, I have seized the opportunity and used it to my advantage.

I have had a lot of support and encouragement from my family and my daughters tell me that I am a successful mother! I am not perfect! But to be less than perfect doesn't mean you are not successful. I always try to set standards for myself that I know I can't meet.

My father has been a major influence in my life, but it wasn't until I was older that I recognised this and how much I have drawn on his wisdom. He taught me the need to value not only others but myself. To respect other people's values even if they are different, to use anger in a positive way and never look back with regret, but to use the experiences constructively. To have a point of view and not be afraid to express it, but above all to listen.

My partner and I now have a successful relationship because we have recognised the power of communication. We also have learnt to value the little time we have together and not put obstacles in each other's way.

SETTING YOUR GOALS

If you have built castles in the air, your work need not be lost: that is where they should be. Now put foundations under them.

Henry David Thoreau

Objective: To set your goals

This section is important because:

— goals give you a sense of direction
— goals keep you moving
— goals determine what you do next

Contents:

— think-through questionnaire
— building on your successes
— vision and sense of direction
— the time of your life
— setting your goals
— is it worth it?
— what are you waiting for?
— summary and action
— profile of Pauline Townsend

Setting your goals

In this section you will be setting your goals, drawing on the work you've already done. The goals can be as ambitious or cautious as you wish, as personal or work-related as you wish, as public or private as you wish.

Goals:

— help clarify your thoughts

— get you started

— save time

— give you the impetus to make changes

— can be changed!

Some people feel uncomfortable about setting goals because:

— it seems like tempting fate

— if they don't reach them, they'll feel a failure

— if they're a success – what next?

— they'd rather just let life happen to them

— they'd rather make it up as they go along

— they're too busy

— they don't have the confidence

How do you feel about setting your goals?

Please when I have something to aim for - look forward too to

Think-through questionnaire

Life for many women is rather like doing a circus balancing act while juggling at the same time! For those setting out on adult life there are so many options to think about and choices to make. Older women have to take account of the consequences of many previous decisions. Take as much time as you need to think about the questions that are important to you.

> The questions are designed to help you think about the different aspects of your life. Use them to clarify your thoughts and spark off ideas to help you in your goals. Skip the sections that don't apply to you.

Money matters

Money matters a great deal to some and not to others. Consider:
— do you have your own income? *Yes*
— if so, how well does your income match your outgoings? *coping at present*
— how do you feel about the difference? *The future concerns me*
— are you the only breadwinner? What does this mean to you? *worries me for the future*
— do you have, or are you considering having, a mortgage? *No*
— how much more do you want to earn? *Continue & earn more than at present aim to bring in £1000 a month.*
— how much less could you manage on if you really needed to or wanted to? *I hope my pens*
— how much money do you want to earn long-term?
— what about a pension? Do you have one? Do you understand it?
— do you have any investments or savings? Do you understand them? *must get more*

Work circumstances

Are you in paid employment? *Yes*
Are you looking for paid employment? *for the future*
How do you feel about working/not working in paid employment? *Its scary but necessary*

How do you want to work?
— full-time? *occasionally*
— part-time? ✓
— job-sharing? ✓
— self-employment or contract working? ✓
— homeworking? ✓

How prepared are you to move for work?
— what daily travelling are you prepared to do?
— how far would you move for the right opportunity?
— how much does your current pension scheme (if you have one) influence your decisions to change work?

If you are thinking of starting your own business or already have one, consider:
— how far down the track are you? *Analysis & train*
— what is the nature of your product or service? *Service & sales*
— what market are you in? *Support industry*
— who specifically are your customers? *small organisations & individuals*

— what do they buy now? *Have difficulty*
— who are your competitors? *forwards etc*
— how will market trends affect your business?
— how will you cope if your income is irregular? *Fall back a pension*

Philosophy of life

Everybody has one, whether it is a deeply held spiritual belief or a catch phrase you run your life by, such as 'Live and let live', or 'Never do harm to anyone'. It may not be something you think about every day.

Ultimately nothing matters. must change this.

— what is your philosophy of life?
— do you have particular religious or spiritual beliefs?
— do you follow any other particular path of development?
— what are you looking for or hoping for?
— what are your views about death?
— have you made a Will?

Living on your own

— is it out of choice, or through special circumstances? *Circumstances*
— what do you enjoy most about living on your own? *freedom of choice*
— what do you like least about living on your own? *Companionship*
— how long do you want to go on living on your own?
— what do your friends/family think about it?
— do they pressurise you to do something different?
— how does it affect you financially?
— how prepared are you to move?
— what do you like to do for holidays? *Meet people*

Considering a close partnership

If you are considering sharing your life with someone else, do you:

— see it as a partnership for life or short-term? *short-term*
— want to live with the person? *No*
— know where you will live? *Here*
— want to share financial arrangements? *No*
— want to have sexual relations?
— want to make it a legal arrangement? (marriage, trust deed)
— feel your freedom being eaten away?
— know what you want out of the relationship?
— know what the other wants?
— know your doubts, fears and hopes?
— share your doubts, fears and hopes with the other?
— love the person? (or are you in love? Or both?)
— know how compatible or complementary your daily rhythms are?
— know how your work patterns relate to each other's?
— know what effect it will have on your social life?
— know how your track record with relationships is influencing you?

Being in a partnership

— how do you feel about your relationship?
— how much respect does your partner show for you?
— to what extent does your sex life satisfy you?
— to what extent do you tolerate verbal, emotional and physical abuse?
— what financial arrangements do you have – separate or joint bank accounts, credit cards, etc?
— how do you share all the expenses: equally? proportionally to your income? pool everything and act as if it's one income?

If your partner earns less than you or is not in paid employment, do you:

— treat all income as joint?
— make clear the differences?
— try to compensate by paying for things quietly or secretly?
— never mention it?
— feel OK about it – or not OK?
— know how your partner really feels about it?

If you earn less than your partner or are not in paid employment, also look at the questions above.

If you both work:

What comes first?
— your work?
— your partner's work?
— your relationship with each other?

How do you see your own work?
— essential financially?
— unimportant for your fulfilment as a person?
— necessary for your development as a person?
— gets in the way of your relationship?
— enhances your relationship?
— stops you being effective in other roles?
— helps you cope with other roles?

How does your partner see your work?
— essential financially?
— unimportant for your fulfilment as a person?
— necessary for your development as a person?
— gets in the way of your relationship?
— enhances your relationship?
— stops you being effective in other roles?
— helps you cope with other roles?

How mobile and flexible are you?
— will move for your own work
— will move for your partner's work

— happy to be away for short spells/longer spells
— happy for your partner to be away for short spells/longer spells
— whose work takes priority?

How mobile and flexible is your partner?
— will move for his/her own work
— will move for your work
— happy to be away for short spells/longer spells
— happy for you to be away for short spells/longer spells
— whose work takes priority?

What about holidays?
— have them together
— have them separate
— it varies

How long do you see your partnership lasting?

— forever
— for quite some time
— ending soon

Considering having children?

— how do you feel about it?
— how does your partner (if you have one) feel?
— what size family do you want?
— how will having children affect your life generally (financially, practically, emotionally)?

What will be the effects on your work of having children?
— types of work
— mobility

What arrangements will be needed for times of ill health?

Who will take what amount of time off around the birth?

Will you and/or your partner take a career break?

How might a career break affect:
— your career?
— your life with the child(ren)?
— your partnership?

What arrangements are needed for child-care?

What if you are unable to have children?
— how might you feel?
— what help will you seek?
— when will you give up trying?
— will you consider adoption?

No children?

- — is this a conscious choice?
- — how do you feel about it?
- — what are the benefits and drawbacks?
- — how do other people treat you as a result?
- — what might change this situation?

Already have children?

Who supports the child(ren) financially?

How do/would you cope with the child(ren) or your partner in the event of:
- — illness in the family?
- — short spells away for work?
- — longer spells away for work?

Who cares for, or will care for, your child(ren) after school and in the school holidays?

If your child is under school age, how effective are your child-care arrangements?

Who arranges babysitters?

Who does the 'thinking' about how the children are looked after?

How does being a working mother appeal to you?

What do you enjoy or look forward to about being a working mother?

What do you need to do to improve things?

Has your child any special needs?

How does this affect your life?

How is your relationship with your child(ren) changing as they grow up?

How do you feel about your child(ren) leaving or having left home?

How does having grown-up child(ren) affect you?

Dependent relative?

What effect does this situation have on your life?
- — financially?
- — emotionally?
- — in terms of time?
- — in terms of mobility?

What special needs does your relative have?

How much are you able to meet the needs yourself?

How are the rest of the needs met?

What support services are available to you?

What further support do you still need?

What changes do you foresee in the immediate future?

How could an organisation's career break scheme help?

What does all this mean?

You have now reviewed some of the personal circumstances about your life which affect your decisions for the future. Jot down here what has come out of this:

— what surprises were there (if any)?

— what questions needed the most thought?

How long am I prepared to stay on my own.

— what needs more thought before you set your goals?

— what do you need to discuss with others before you set your goals?

— what do you want to change?

Discuss any issues that have arisen from this think-through questionnaire with the people involved or someone who can help you digest the questions and answers that have been provoked.

Building on your successes

Before you set your goals, one more aspect will influence them – your track record and view of success. Whenever you feel successful, it boosts your confidence and spurs you on.

What does success mean to you?

Jot down ideas of what success is for you – add at least five ideas:

Success is *bringing up my children to be responsible adults*

Success is *being the first woman on the Board of Directors*

Success is having enough money to live on comfortably

Success is feeling secure

Success is a sense of wellbeing

Success is being organised

Success is a lovely home

Success is friends

Success is places to go

Success is people around me

What does it mean?

Each woman has her own personal blend of definitions of success. Check that yours are specific, eg: to write 'success is being happy' is very general – what do you mean by 'being happy'?

Notice how many of them you are already achieving.

Transfer your personal definition of success to page 254 in your personal resource bank.

Vision and sense of direction

The questions in the think-through questionnaire are designed to further your thinking about your personal circumstances, and the choices that you have open to you, whether you opt for them or not. You may already be very clear about what you want to do (that may be why you're working with this Workbook), but if you're not, consider two different approaches – being a person who has a vision, or a person who has a sense of direction.

Vision

Some people are natural visionaries. They often see things in their heads, and can actually describe the picture to others. Others may have a vision which drives them on of how life could be (of a social evil put right, or a world based on different values). It is this vision which inspires and energises them, so they are motivated by achieving, in whatever measure, the vision that they have. Have a go at being a visionary:

Your vision of the future

Let go of any doubts, hurdles, fears or thoughts. In a consciously optimistic frame of mind, build a picture that is as detailed and as positive as you can make it. Let yourself go and let your imagination run riot. Imagine how you would like a day in your life to be in 5 years time and use the questions on the following pages to give you some ideas. Deliberately go over the top with your picture.

Jot down notes, or ...

Write the story of it like a magazine article, or ...

Tell the story to someone else as if it was what you are going to do tomorrow or ..

Paint the picture – take a large sheet of paper and paint or colour your future day in any way you like.

① 65 May 2002 already selling + day webs
2 66 2003   ③ 67 2004   ④ 68 2005   ⑤ 69 2006

Think about:
— where are you? Which country, town, village? What sort of place, building, countryside? How is the scene? Well kept, desolate, palatial?

In my house on the River with my rich husband.

— what are you doing?

sitting in the garden with friends watching the boats go by.

— who's with you?

my husband, his sister & her husband their children & grandchildren Nick & Sarah, Jeff & Catrinal & their little girl. My husbands 3 Children & their partners, and 2 grandchildren to his Second Son & his wife

— what is fulfilling about your life?

I have found the family I have to belong too

— what fun are you having?

Its my husband's birthday - hes a year older than I.

— why is it fun?

Because family Stories are being swapped

— what are you good at?

entertaining & giving parties, & getting everyon to join in.

— how do you feel about it?. *Very relaxed and happy.*

— Any of the answers to these questions could become goals.

Sense of direction

Other people have no vision, but are equally motivated by a commitment to a WAY of doing things, which gives them a strong sense of direction. They know which way to go and how to make choices day-to-day. They know that if they are prepared they will be ready to take opportunities as they arise.

If you're more a 'direction' type of person, or are still unsure of your overall goals, then consider these questions to sharpen up your direction.

— what makes you really angry? *Seeing damaging parenting in shops cruelty, greed, unfairness injustice, all the 'bad' things*

— what do you get really excited about? *Teaching or showing people something, doing or making something creatively beautiful*

— if you were to die today, what would you regret not having achieved? *The tidying up. The nice house, the organisation, carpets clothes etc - not finished*

— what ambitions do you have that remain unfulfilled? Think back to your childhood ambitions – any unfulfilled ambition will give you clues. *Living in London ✓ Working in London ✓ Second husband*

— what unfulfilled dreams do you have? No matter how crazy or outlandish. *my house on the River, Lottery, 2nd husband rich, big No garden, Orient Express, Concorde, more travel*

— what are your deepest held values? See page 56. Are they being met? *NO*

— are you spending the time of your life as you would wish? If not, what do you want to do about it? *NOT FEEL ITS ALL IMPOSSIBLE*

The time of your life

If your answer to the last question was 'No' then take another look at how you're spending your time now.

This circle represents all your time and energy excluding sleeping. Think about three categories of use for this time and energy. You can subdivide these main categories if you want to; these are just to get you started.

WORK = time spent on your paid or unpaid employment or full-time education *7·30 am to 4·30 pm - 1 hour free midday 4.30 - 6-30 food* *5½ 2½ 8 hours*

HOME = time spent on maintaining the home and family, ie: duties, chores, visiting relatives, taking the children to school *④ 2 hrs am 2 hrs pm*

LEISURE = time spent on yourself or doing things you enjoy (this includes your 'me time') *Guilt time 6·30 - 8·30 TV ②*

Divide the circle into proportions that show how you'd LIKE life to be:

SLEEP 8.30 pm - 5.30 am ⑨

Sa + Sun, inefficient, tired

Up & dress 2 hours
8 hours Sleep
8 hour Work

mid night
10.30

5 hours
2 x ½ hours

WORK 2 Me TV Cost
Sleep
up. 6·30
Clothes down before
1 Thing per day
Papers daily
doing supper at table
Watch specific TV

Up wash dress out
Noon
5½
8 hours
Chores

Now repeat the same exercise, dividing up the circle into how it actually is at the moment. Take an overview of how it feels, don't start doing elaborate time logs!

Take a look at what you've drawn – where are the conflicts between the two circles? While it's fresh in your head, jot down the aspects of your use of time that you'd like to change. These may spur you on and become goals:

I'm spending far too much time on housework — I really would like to cut that down.

Cut down sleep time — arrange day better; House Time label + budget

The dream/reality gap

Between the dreams of the future and the reality of the present there is often a gap. If the gap seems very big or insurmountable then it puts people off trying. When you look at the gap you can:

— find choices where there appears to be no choice
— look for the first simple steps to take you in the right direction
— challenge your assumptions about your constraints

YOU HAVE MUCH MORE FREEDOM THAN YOU THINK

Setting your goals

Take your dream seriously. You are here to become the best you can be. You owe it to yourself.

Susan Hayward, *Begin it now*

Set whatever goals you want to:

— short-term and long-term
— serious and more lighthearted
— connected with work and connected with home
— just for you and involving other people
— outrageous and conventional
— upfront and secret
— within your current organisation and outside of it
— within the familiar and going out into the unknown

One good tip is to set a mixture – it will make life more interesting, and when you get stuck with one you can take action on another.

Follow the charts on the next pages. They break into four categories:

— goals for work
— goals for your relationships
— goals just for you
— goals related to the world

In the first column put the overall goal – just a line or two on your overall objective.

In the second column break the goal down into all the small, individual actions you will have to take to achieve the goal – be as detailed as you can.

For example, to achieve this goal:

— what skills will you need?
— what qualifications will you need?
— how much money will you need?
— what relationships will you need?
— what motivation and determination will you need?
— what will you need to change in yourself?
— what will you have to give up, in order to achieve this?
— what information will you need?

In the third column, consider the possible consequences for you and other people if you choose this goal.

Have a go – after all you're not carving in granite – it's just a bit of paper and you can always change it!

YOUR GOALS AT WORK

GOAL	ACTION NEEDED – BY WHEN	POSSIBLE CONSEQUENCES
Investigate changing jobs	Get information about other companies locally by 25th February Survey Situations Vacant for one month from 14th January Talk to Angus about the implications Apply for at least four jobs to get job application experience by 28th February Explore at least one totally different work area	Make a fresh start Work longer hours/shorter hours Chance of greater satisfaction Risk of failure Get out of my rut Move to new location
Have portfolio of opportunities on retirement.	List possibilities Create folder ea with degree in filing cabinet for each Gather treasury info Gather Networks & mentors where possible Set aside study Time Prepare proposals, feasibility Write to Ace Maddingley Long Eland re with for Mary	feel more secure meet more people develop my esteem meet people – prepare to be hassled

YOUR GOALS IN YOUR RELATIONSHIPS

GOAL	ACTION NEEDED – BY WHEN	POSSIBLE CONSEQUENCES
Decide whether to go on living with Jeff	*Set aside time to think – 14th May* *Sort out possible alternative place to live by 23rd June* *Talk to Jeff to find out how he feels*	*I break the deadlock and clear the air* *I feel better* *It might make it worse* *I might make a fool of myself*
Be the person I wd need to be to attract the person I want. I've got to go out & meet people - bey the person I could be	House Garden me Clothes etc a la Anthony Robbins I feel better all ready	

YOUR GOALS JUST FOR YOU

GOAL	ACTION NEEDED – BY WHEN	POSSIBLE CONSEQUENCES
More time to myself	Say No to going to pub – by 1st April Talk to the family about my needs – by 28th June Set aside 'Me time' daily – by 31st March Enrol at public library – by 16th Sept	I'll be more relaxed Other people will have less of my time I may feel guilty
I've set up time Schedule	Will continue with lists to do & time Table	I will feel less stressed

YOUR GOALS TO HELP THE WORLD

GOAL	ACTION NEEDED – BY WHEN	POSSIBLE CONSEQUENCES
Reduce my contribution to pollution	Take paper and bottles for recycling – weekly Find out what the greenhouse effect really is – 21st November Start buying biodegradable washing up liquid and other products – 16th December	Feel better Save some trees Know what further action to take Will cost more More hassle when shopping Could be expensive
Recycle everything.	Stamps Paper	

Is it worth it?

Having set your goals, look back at what you've written, think about the consequences of all the hard work you've committed yourself to, and ask yourself the one last question: Is it worth it?

It is magnicantly worth it – it is who I am I feel it

If the answer is 'No' then you have set inappropriate goals, set them too high, or with inappropriate deadlines. Go back and amend your sheets until the answer is 'Yes' because the answer has to be 'Yes' for you to carry on.

Reaching 'YES' means you've reached the point of commitment.

It's one thing to write down goals and know what you want to do with them. It's another matter to get started and keep going. That takes commitment.

— Commitment turns ideas into action

— Commitment changes wishes into intentions

— Commitment takes courage and determination

— Commitment has to be renewed each day

— Commitment means you put your energy into it

This is the point to take the plunge and commit yourself to action or go back and work through earlier sections again.

I am committed & will suceed

What are you waiting for?

— the children to leave home/start school?
— the boss to retire?
— to win the Lottery?
— for someone else to encourage you?
— for someone to make it safe for you?
— to lose weight?
— to feel ready?
— for someone to die?
— for someone to give you permission?
— for a kick?
— to get your qualification?
— for the perfect job?
— to stop feeling guilty?
— for your knight in shining armour?
— to stop feeling frightened?

Real reason or EXCUSE

It's easy to stop yourself setting goals or taking steps to achieve them if you think you have a good reason not to do it now. There may be very valid reasons why you cannot do something now, but just check that it's a real reason and not an excuse.

You may be working through this Workbook because you feel you don't have any goals, so if you *still* feel that you don't have a goal, then setting a goal becomes your goal! In which case do the following exercise:

> Go back to the goal setting charts on pages 118–121, and write 'setting a goal' as your goal and then list all the actions that you need to take in order to set a goal such as: talking to someone, finding out information, setting aside time to think, or whatever.
>
> Then set yourself a date to review your progress.

> One way to help your commitment to your goals is to share them with someone who will support and encourage you. Have a conversation with someone you can trust to strengthen your commitment.

Don't be afraid to take a big step if one is indicated. You can't cross a chasm in two small jumps.

David Lloyd George

Having done that — stop!

CONGRATULATIONS! You have now achieved what for most people is the most difficult part of personal development – setting goals. For most people, having the imagination and the determination to decide what to do is half the battle.

Now you've decided what you're going to do, the next step is to find how to do it!

> Before you move on, have a celebration – whatever you like. Award yourself a treat – an evening off, a long bubble bath, a drink with a friend – anything!
>
> It's important that you acknowledge the importance of what you've just done, not to frighten yourself but to give yourself a pat on the back!

A JOURNEY OF 1,000 MILES STARTS WITH A SINGLE STEP

Summary and action

In this section, you've been asked to consider a great number of issues. You've thought about whether you have vision or direction, and you've set your goals.

both

Your personal resource bank

Take your goal-setting further, and record your overall, long-term goals.

Further optional reading

Look for inspiration in the biographies of others.

Action

What action will you now take to start achieving your goals? Take each goal, and decide ONE SMALL THING you will do over the next week to make a start.

Nothing is too small to be a start.

I will _Recreate Weight Watchers & lose 5lb_ by _next Sunday_

I will _Order carpets_ by _on Tuesday_

I will _Write Ace, Maddingley & Long Road_ by _Sunday an_

I will _begin my time schedule_ by _Sunday ie start No_

Profile

Pauline Townsend
Revenue Protection Inspector, British Rail

I was born in 1950, the youngest of four, my eldest sibling being over twenty years older than me. My very first memory is my mother screaming at me 'Your brother was a mistake and you're a bloody catastrophe.' I grew up to be a lonely, unconfident teenager, who had problems relating to others and who left school at fifteen being unable to read, write or do simple arithmetic.

My first job was in Woolworths and I was sacked after a few weeks when they realised my incompetence. I then worked in various factories, never staying longer than a couple of months in any one place, afraid they would find out how stupid I was. Fortunately for me this was a time of full employment, when one could leave one job and find and start another within hours.

Six weeks after meeting John we were married. I was nineteen. A year later I had our daughter and I settled down to be a wife and mother intending never to work again. I felt safe with my small group of family and friends. When my daughter was about six I realised that she was having problems at school and because of my own literacy problems I was unable to help her. I therefore went back to school and within two years I was not only reading and writing but teaching literacy to other adults having successfully undertaken a training course which enabled me to do so.

Learning point: You never know what you can do until you try.

About ten years ago I had to go back to work. I did not want to as I still did not have enough confidence to undertake a job with responsibilities, so I went back to factory work. If I'd had a choice I would not have gone back to work at all but we desperately needed the money.

About a year later, after gaining some confidence, (after all I had been working and they had not sacked me) I applied for a job with British Rail and, much to my astonishment, I was successful. My duties were cleaning, answering customer enquiries and seeing trains safely away from the station.

Some three months later my supervisor advised me to seek promotion; I applied for a position as a train guard and I got it.

Learning point: Accept other people's confidence in you – they may believe in you more than you believe in yourself.

The training for a guard is quite intensive, lasting some six weeks and then on-the-job training. I remained doing platform duties for a couple of months while waiting for a training place and in that time I took every opportunity to talk to established guards, asking questions, but also just getting to know some of them. I'm glad I did so because I was to spend nearly a year as the only woman at a depot of almost 140 men and already knowing some of them helped considerably.

Learning point: What I call chatting, some call networking and it's never a waste of time.

My next position was as a conductor and for the last 15 months or so I've been doing my present job. I now feel it's time to move on but because of the recession fewer people are leaving the industry, therefore there is less opportunity for promotion, and although I now feel confident enough to look outside of British Rail for a job, again there is not much going, especially for people like myself with no qualifications.

I'm now in my second year of studying with the Open University working towards qualifications but in the meantime I have not given up – I keep looking and I'm determined to use all my experience and the people I know to help me find another job which will add to the experience I already have.

Learning point: Never give up.

I have already decided that I can afford to take a small pay cut and if need be I am prepared to work for less money, provided I think this will benefit me in the future.

Learning point: Decide what you want and what you are prepared to give up to achieve it, then go for it.

GETTING INFORMATION

7

As a rule he (or she) who has the most information will have the greater success in life.

Benjamin Disraeli

Objective: To get the right information to enable you to achieve your plans

This section is important because:

— information minimises risk and increases certainty
— the right information gives you confidence, enthusiasm, energy and ideas
— information increases awareness
— looking for information lets other people know you're interested

Contents:

— information you need
— where to start looking
— your information map
— summary and action
— profile of Elizabeth Standen

Getting information

When you set off on a long and hazardous journey, you would be ill advised to set off without doing your homework. This section is about getting the information you will need to get there. It is also about keeping your eyes and ears open.

Information minimises your risk and increases your chances of certainty. How much risk you take is up to you. If you wait until you have 100% certainty you may never move. If you move with a 10% chance of success, you need to know what you are doing. Information is about maximising chances of success.

Information is about energising you too.

Seeking information means:

— using your contacts

— asking questions

— knowing where to start

— picking people's brains

— asking advice

— seeing the connections and implications of random bits of information

— interpreting what you observe

— becoming a detective!

INFORMATION EMPOWERS YOU

Information you need

The information you need will, of course, depend on what you want to achieve. However, the goals you set yourself may well be influenced by the information you discover! So it's catch 22! You set your goals in Section 6 so now find out everything you need to know to help you achieve these goals. As you get new information you may need to go back and amend your goals.

Here are some categories to help you think about the information you will need to achieve your goals. Use these lists to generate ideas for the exercise that follows:

Information about your organisation or prospective organisation, such as:

— the objectives of the organisation

— the organisation's circumstances – booming, declining, under threat, part of a bigger organisation

— the structure of the organisation

— the policy and practice on equal opportunities, maternity leave, childcare, career breaks etc.

— the opportunities for flexible working, such as job sharing

— career opportunities

— training opportunities

— the position of women in the organisation, and the routes they took to get there

Information about qualifications, such as:

— the professional qualifications that are valued by your organisation or prospective organisation

— the support that your organisation would give you to study

— the different ways of gaining the qualification

— people who have already got the qualification you're interested in

— the time and money it would take

— how to enrol

Information about your personal circumstances

— money

— housing

— care facilities for friends, relatives, and/or yourself

— child-care

— transport

— any form of abuse – yours or others

— your job mobility – real and perceived

Information about yourself

— health

— your interests

— how your decisions affect others

— how you come across to other people – at home and at work

Information for your goals

Draw up your own list of the things you'll need to know to help you achieve your goals. Don't worry if you don't know where to find the information yet – write down everything:

Information you must have:

Promoting myself
Visability
Marketing

Social Groups, Write to all Recourses at back of book

Go thro my retirement stuff again

Information you would like to have:

Who else is doing what I want to do

Information it would be nice to have if you have time:

Where to start looking

There are four ways of finding information, through:

— people

— published material

— organisations

— being alert

Information through people

All the people you thought about in Section 5 are potential suppliers of information. People are the key – they open or close the doors on the information you need.

Ask advice, pick brains and request feedback. You've got nothing to lose and very few people will refuse to help – it's up to you to make the first move. The list below is a prompt to increase your information network:

Bosses: ex-, present, potential, and boss's boss

Colleagues: ex-, present, potential

Officials: personnel managers
                  training officers
                  trade union representatives
                  organisers of clubs and societies
                  solicitors
                  librarians
                  counsellors
                  doctors
                  the tutor of your evening class

Other potential
allies: friends, family, partners, mentors, acquaintances, people you've
                  met on courses, at parties, on holiday, people you've heard of
                  doing things that could help you, people who are doing things
                  that you want to do.

Yvonne: I greatly admired the woman Factory Manager on my site who I knew had started off at the same level as me. I plucked up courage one day to ask her how she'd done it. It turned out that her major step forward meant her working in a totally different region for three years, so that she could come back at a higher level. I hadn't considered that before, and am now looking at sideways moves for myself.

Information through published material

There's masses around, whether it's on computer, audio cassette, video or in conventional print.

Handbooks and Booklets:

directories of trusts which
    give grants
staff handbooks
career guides
directories
equal opportunities booklets
brochures by organisations
college prospectuses

Information on:

women's development
managerial and technical skills
setting up your own business
autobiographies
professional skills
health
academic life

Newspapers and Magazines:

national and local newspapers
trade or specialist interest magazines
annual reports
in-house magazines
professional newsletters
the Springboard newsletter – NewsSplash

Other media:

the Internet
TV, radio, film, video, microfilm
computer-based information
documentaries
training films
distance-learning materials
TAP information services about local training
courses in your local library
mailing lists
audio cassettes

Information through organisations

There are lots of organisations which specialise in the information you need for your goals. The best starting place for information is usually your local reference library. The appendix gives a number of organisations which may help you.

> Make and keep contacts with the ones that will point you in the right direction.

Government Departments:

County Councils
District Councils
Enterprise Agencies
Small Firms Information Bureaux
TECs

Special interest groups:

professional groups
networking groups
sports and social clubs
churches
Parent Teacher Associations
trade unions
pressure groups

Voluntary Organisations:

Citizens Advice Bureaux
Charities: your reference library has details of
local and national advisory bodies

Information through being alert:

This is all about watching, listening and tuning in to what is going on around you. Pick up the signals and clues to changes. Listen for the opportunities. In particular assess and draw your own conclusions from what happens when:

— a woman applies for a senior post
— you meet someone doing what you want to do
— people gossip
— people show emotion at work
— people get news of changes
— someone leaves suddenly
— someone is pregnant
— someone tries to do something different

Your information map

Take one piece of information you need for a goal – write it in the box in the middle, and then, under the categories, say what you will do to seek out information about this subject. Be ingenious in the ways you approach it. Be prepared to follow up unusual clues. The next page gives a blank chart – photocopy it before you write on it so you can use it for several different subjects. Read the example first — then have a go!

People

Talk to Alwena who runs her own business
Talk to an accountant
General chat with my bank manager
Check what my partner thinks and feels about my ideas

Published material

Booklets from the bank
Newsletter from Women in Enterprise
Read 'Starting your own Business' from the Consumers Association

Starting my own business

Being alert

Keep an eye on similar businesses in the area
Look in newspapers to spot trends
Listen for people talking about what I might provide

Organisations

Go to a meeting of the local Small Business Club
Find my nearest Enterprise Agency
Phone the Small Firms Information Service

People	**Published material**
Being alert	**Organisations**
People	**Published material**

Summary and action

In this section you have identified the information you need to achieve your goals.

Some of the information you collect will confirm that you are travelling in the right direction. Other information may make you change your mind. The point of getting the information is to help you make decisions about the route.

Further optional reading

The appendix for useful sources of information.

Action

Here are some suggestions:

— read a different newspaper to get a different perspective, or start reading one if you don't now
— talk to your manager about the effect of the European Union on your organisation
— pick up a totally unusual magazine or book at random and see what it contains that's relevant to your goals
— go to a women's network meeting to see if you like it
— continue pursuing your information 'musts' from page 130
— visit your reference library

I will _____ by _____

I will _____ by _____

I will _____ by _____

I will _____ by _____

Profile

Elizabeth Standen
Equalities Officer, Bristol City Council

When I left school aged seventeen, I was classified as of only average intelligence, medically frail and unemployable. For the next eleven years I stayed at home, only going out when someone pushed me in a wheelchair.

Then quite suddenly things began to change! I had been trying to join an evening class to do 'O' level English, but had been rejected. 'You might fall down the stairs', 'You wouldn't be able to keep up', 'We couldn't teach a blind person'. The excuses rained down.

Then one evening I was visited by the Director of Studies. 'The evening class is full, but there are places on the day release course. Someone would have to come and look after you. If you could arrange that, we'll see what can be done.' So a neighbour and I joined an English Language and Literature class for four hours each Tuesday. I did not expect to take or pass the exam, but it was somewhere to go, once a week. Something to do each day, goals in the shape of homework assignments to aim at.

Learning point: Short term goals keep you moving and can lead to significant achievements.

Around the same time, I heard a talk about the Long-Cane on the radio. It was described as a Mobility Method particularly useful for older people. I was not old, but I was supposed to be frail; perhaps the Long-Cane might give me the means of leaving the house alone? I approached my social worker requesting the training, to be met with a blanket refusal. 'You wouldn't be able to manage it dear!' I had to convince the social services that I *could* manage it.

One day I slipped out of the house while Mum was busy in the kitchen. I found the front gate, and groped and stumbled my way nearly to the end of the road, following walls, hedges and gates. Over the next few weeks I learnt my way round the block, till at last I could do the circuit in 35 minutes.

Learning point: Do not accept the restraints which others place upon you.

At the same time I rang the social worker's office at half past nine every Monday and Thursday morning with the same request. 'Can I have Long-Cane training?' Then an opportunity came my way. Mum was stopped by a woman in the next road, one day on her way to the shops. 'Is it your Elizabeth I've seen going round the block?' 'Yes she's started going for walks.' That evening the woman told her husband 'I was right, it *was* the little blind girl from the next road going round the block.' Her husband was the Director of Social Services for our area. He began to think more seriously about my request for mobility training.

Then one morning, the secretary who took my repeated calls casually commented that it wasn't mobility training I needed, but rehabilitation. 'If her mother died or left home, she'd starve, or have to go into a home.' This casual remark started the social worker thinking. One day she came to see me, and asked if I would like to go to Clifton Spinney, a Social Rehabilitation Centre where I could learn to cook, shop, clean a house and do Long-Cane Training. Later, she told me that they had bets in the office as to whether I would agree to go. Those who put their money on me going won. I went!

Learning point: You may have to make yourself known if you want something to change.

One day that August I was up to my elbows in flour baking a cake, when the phone call came through telling me that I had two 'O' levels in English Language and English Literature.

In November I went to the residential Further Education College where over the following two and a half years I gained four more 'O' levels and two 'A' levels. Then came University. I did not take a job related degree, as I was still believed to be unemployable. Therefore, I was determined on enjoying myself. Throughout my life until then I had been considered pedantic, argumentative and nit-picking. These traits were applauded by my lecturers. Philosophy was obviously the right subject for me. In those three years I learnt to examine arguments with minute care, an invaluable asset when picking your way among the minefields which strew the path of anyone working in the field of equal opportunities.

Learning point: Turn your qualities into strengths.

Towards the end of my degree I visited the Careers Officers, not really expecting to be taken seriously. To my surprise, Veronica seemed to think I would make a good employee, pointing out that I had stayed the course, had little or no time off for illness, and was expected to get a good degree. Her confidence was cheering, but reality wasn't so easy.

I began to think about becoming a solicitor, but I didn't have much of a feel for what solicitors did. I researched the areas of work, visiting the Local Authority Legal Department. I spoke to a solicitor working for a private firm, visited a blind woman working in a busy London Legal Advice Centre, then applied to the Law Society for permission to enrol for the two year post graduate training course. This is usually a formality, but I was disabled, so I had to go to London for a personal interview.

At last I arrived at Manchester Poly clutching my Law Society Authorisation. Two years hard grind later, I emerged with the first year exams carefully passed, but I had only passed four of the seven second year examinations.

Then disaster crowded in, and I spent the next eight and a half months in hospital. It took me eighteen months to regain my physical strength and my confidence. I decided to have another go at the Law exams, and a solicitor offered me two days a week voluntary work in her office to reinforce the correspondence course I was taking. One evening on the train home, I met Veronica who told me about a specialist careers guidance data collecting service being set up to help disabled graduates. They were looking for two graduates with disabilities to do the work.

Learning point: Keep your networks going.

So in March 1985 I began work on a community programme project in Nottingham. Everyone thought I was mad to leave my flat in a town where I had many friends, to go after a one year community programme job which paid less than I had got on Supplementary Benefit. But it was a job, and I was on my way.

Learning point: Sometimes it's necessary to take a drop in income to get you where you want to be.

The one year contract turned into an interesting job, which expanded from data gathering into a full careers guidance service. I might have stayed there for the rest of my working life but three and a half years later I was jolted out of my comfortable existence by redundancy. I was scared!

My first job had only been available to a disabled graduate, but now I had to compete in the open job market. Perhaps no-one would want me. I scoured the papers for suitable posts, preferably in or around Nottingham for I had now bought my first house. I eventually succeeded in getting the job of Disability Officer for a local authority in the north east. Three years later, I moved to Bristol where I now work for the City Council in the Equalities Unit.

I help to develop and implement equalities policies, aimed at ensuring that disabled people have a fair chance of gaining jobs and promotion within the Council, and equal access to all Council Services with all the other groups within the local community. I hope to be working on a broader range of Equalities issues soon, including those concerning black people and women.

Alongside my intellectual search, I was also expanding my social experiences. Within a year of going to college I had met and married the man who supported and pushed me for the next five years. Charles was the first person who appeared to notice that I was an interesting woman as well as a potential brain. Sadly he died six weeks after my graduation, but he had given me an invaluable belief in my own worth. I also wanted to succeed in order to prove that his belief in me was correct.

The last eight years since I started work have not always been easy, but they have been stimulating and challenging. I have had many successes, but also some failures. Throughout it all I have always moved on and up.

When things go wrong, I don't allow myself to brood for long, I try to understand what went wrong, so that it does not happen again.

I have had to learn to know when to continue the fight, and when to quit.

I have discovered that it is not shameful to seek help when one is feeling low.

I have also come to see that work has to be balanced by play. Too much work can make Jill a dull girl and affects your ability to do a good job. Living alone, I found it difficult to stop myself working, so I had to create an alternative demand, and for me this was gardening. Four years ago I bought a greenhouse, arguing that if I planted seeds, I would feel obliged to tend the plants. This year I had courgettes, tomatoes, peppers and aubergines coming out of my ears! I have also started to write seriously. When, as a child, if asked what I was going to do when I grew up I always replied, 'Write books.' Perhaps I will after all.

Learning point: Listen to your childhood ambitions. Never give up.

THE ASSERTIVE YOU

No-one can make you feel inferior without your consent.

Eleanor Roosevelt

Objective: To equip you with knowledge and understanding of assertiveness and build your confidence in being assertive

This section is important because:

— assertiveness enables you to deal with difficult situations
— assertiveness makes communication more effective
— there are lots of misunderstandings about assertiveness
— you need to decide for yourself which situations you want to work on

Contents:

— why bother with assertiveness?
— what assertiveness is and is not
— assertiveness in practice
— your assertiveness agenda
— fight/flight syndrome
— how to be assertive
— finding the right words
— tone of voice and body language
— summary and action
— profile of Mary Nelson

The assertive you

Assertiveness forms a major part of this Workbook because many women say they would like to change the way they deal with situations.

This section builds up an understanding of assertiveness so you can develop your own skills further.

Assertiveness receives a lot of publicity, some good, some bad, and some downright misleading, so many people have very mixed feelings about it. However, your ability to assert yourself affects everything else you do and don't do, from day-to-day activities right through to major life decisions. So it's important to understand what it is and what you want to do with it. The questionnaire you completed on page 79 will have given you some clues about your usual ways of responding in a variety of situations.

Why bother with assertiveness?

By behaving assertively:

— your self-confidence increases

— you are properly understood

— other people know exactly where they are with you

— you are more open to receiving feedback

— your relationships are based on reality rather than illusion

— you stand a better chance of getting what you want

— you feel better for expressing your feelings

— you have fewer situations that are unresolved

— even if you do not resolve a situation, you feel better for having tried

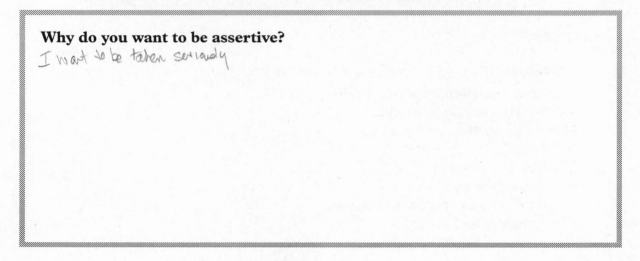

Why do you want to be assertive?

I want to be taken seriously

What assertiveness is and is not

People often confuse aggressive and assertive behaviour. So when they think of developing assertiveness skills they worry about being seen as aggressive.

It is important to define what we mean. It's helpful to define aggressive and passive behaviour – as these are the ones that most of us seem to experience day-to-day – and then go on to clarify assertive behaviour.

Write down your own definitions of what aggressive, passive and assertive behaviour is here. Not the dictionary definitions – your own personal views.

Being aggressive is:

attacking

Being passive is:

letting people walk over me

Being assertive is:

Expecting a reasonable response to my needs

Have a look now at these notes about each behaviour, to see how your definitions compare.

Aggressive behaviour is:

— getting your own way, no matter what

— getting your own point across at other people's expense

— getting people to do things they don't want to do

— being loud and violent

— interrupting others

— winning at all costs

Recognise any of this? It's important to notice that we're talking about aggressive *behaviour* here, and not aggressive people, as we are all capable of behaving aggressively, passively and assertively.

Not all aggressive behaviour is obvious or direct. There is also indirect aggressive behaviour which can be:

— conveyed in a polite way

— quiet and apparently inoffensive

— manipulating or tricking people

— ignoring people

— being silent

— using sarcasm

— putting people down, making them feel small

— inoffensive on the surface

Most people have a tendency towards one form of behaviour rather than another, and vary their behaviour depending on the situation and their feelings at the time.

Aggressive behaviour doesn't come from being over-confident – quite the reverse; it comes from lack of confidence and fear. Underneath the blustery bully is a coward. It may be difficult to believe, but the more senior person who's having a go at you is a real person underneath, who's feeling just as scared or threatened as a person behaving passively.

Think about occasions at home and work when you have behaved aggressively.

Think about occasions at home and work when other people have behaved aggressively towards you.

ASSERTIVENESS IS ABOUT RESPECTING OTHER PEOPLE

Passive behaviour is:

— keeping quiet for fear of upsetting people

— avoiding conflict

— saying yes when you want to say no

— always putting other people's needs first

— not expressing your feelings

— going along with things you don't like or agree with

— apologising excessively

— inwardly burning with anger and frustration

— being vague about your ideas and what you want

— justifying your actions to other people

— appearing indecisive

Ever found yourself doing any of this? Most women find themselves using passive behaviour quite a lot. If so, you may have reached the point where you don't know what your views or feelings on a topic are, but somehow you have a vague feeling of dissatisfaction at being taken for granted, or not taken seriously.

Passive behaviour stems from lack of confidence. Turning passive behaviour into assertive behaviour will gradually build your confidence.

Think about occasions at home and work when you have behaved passively.

Think about occasions at home and work when you have experienced someone behaving passively towards you.

What is it that you want to change about your behaviour?

Act more professionally, with concentration

ASSERTIVENESS IS ABOUT BUILDING YOUR OWN SELF-RESPECT

Assertive behaviour is:

— being open and honest with yourself and other people

— listening to other people's points of view

— showing understanding of other people's situations

— expressing your ideas clearly, but not at the expense of others

— being able to reach workable solutions to difficulties

— making decisions – even if your decision is not to make a decision!

— being clear about your point and not being sidetracked

— dealing with conflict

— having self-respect and respect for other people

— being equal with others and retaining your uniqueness

— expressing feelings honestly and with care

How often are you truly assertive by these standards? Most people find they can be assertive in some types of situations but tend to be aggressive or passive in others.

Are there any patterns or themes in the way you deal with situations? What are they?

At work I'm very assertive but at home my aggression comes out.

Throughout this Workbook we are using the following definition of assertiveness:

 Assertiveness is a form of behaviour which demonstrates your self-respect and respect for others. Assertiveness is also concerned with dealing with your own feelings about yourself and other people, as much as with the end result.

Think about occasions at home and work when you have behaved truly assertively.

Think about occasions at home and work when you felt someone was being truly assertive with you.

ASSERTIVENESS IS ABOUT DEALING WITH YOUR FEELINGS

Assertiveness in practice

Does assertiveness always work? It depends on your objectives. It doesn't guarantee a particular outcome but if the process is followed it usually makes you feel that speaking up for yourself and expressing your feelings was worthwhile.

For example: Your boss asks you to stay late to finish a piece of work and you are perfectly assertive in your refusal to stay. Your boss isn't in the least impressed, and still insists despite your explanation. Ultimately she still insists and unless you feel like resigning over it you realise that you will have to stay late. Your assertiveness hasn't affected the outcome – you still stay late.

However, behaving assertively in that situation has helped in a number of ways:

— You preserve your self-esteem: 'At least I said what I felt and explained properly without getting upset.'

— No one can ever say that you meekly agreed: 'You never said anything last time.'

— You may have provoked your boss into re-assessing you: 'I didn't realise she felt so strongly about that, she's got more to her than I thought.'

For the rest of this section and the next you will be looking at developing your assertive behaviour in a way that feels appropriate to you. It doesn't mean turning shy people into raving extroverts and it doesn't mean turning zany, fun people into boring grey clones.

Your assertiveness agenda

Write down the real situations that you encounter, either at work or at home, where you would like to be more assertive. Start off with one that isn't very frightening at all. You could probably deal with it if you just got on with it:

Go to the other extreme, and think of the most difficult or frightening situation that you encounter, or that you are avoiding. It may be something that makes you feel quite ill to think about, and you may think that nothing can be done about it. Write it down, all the same:

Prompts

On the next page you will be asked to write down more situations in which you want to become more assertive.

Here are some examples of the types of situations other women have chosen to work on. They are not in any order of difficulty because what may be easy for one woman may be the most difficult for another, and the other way round. They are given purely as prompts to help you think of your own situations. Cover them up if you don't want to be prompted.

Personal

— dealing with comments about living alone

— stopping my elderly mother from going out half-dressed

— telling my friend I only want her to stay for a week and not blaming anyone else for asking her to go

— asking my family to tidy up after themselves without nagging or getting angry

— dealing with a racist comment on the bus

— getting the children to close doors and switch off lights

— putting my needs first for once

— getting my mortgage increased

— telling my partner how I feel about his/her abusiveness

— having some time to myself each day/week

— talking to my landlord about getting repairs done

Work

— working hours interfering with home life

— saying no to requests for help when I'm overloaded

— colleagues not taking turns to make tea

— refusing to help Joyce out again with her schedules

— speaking up at meetings

— standing up for what I believe in with more senior people

— persuading my boss to let me do some of her work

— dealing with a colleague who I know is lying to me

— being sexually harassed at work

— being asked at an interview why I should get the job

Your assertiveness agenda

On page 145 you wrote down an easy and a very difficult situation in which you want to be more assertive.

Transfer the easy one to No 1 and the difficult one to No 10 on this page. Now think of more situations. Make the low numbers the easier situations and the high numbers the more difficult ones.

Think of as many different situations as you can. Try to get a mixture of: home/work, friends/relatives, big/little, short term/long term situations – use the prompt sheet on the previous page if you need more ideas.

Next to each one write down how you deal with them now (passively, aggressively, indirectly aggressively).

1

2

3

4

5

6

7

8

9

10

ASSERTIVENESS ENABLES EACH OF US TO BE MORE OURSELVES

Fight/flight syndrome

By definition, the list of 10 situations that you've just compiled are those when you do not behave assertively. Sometimes people are docile at work and bad tempered at home, or doormats at home and downright bossy at work. Most people swing between aggressiveness and passiveness.

The fight/flight syndrome can explain your response to difficult situations.

Our bodies have evolved to help us deal with physical danger when we are faced with a difficult situation. They instinctively respond by putting us into a physically alert state (ie: heart pounding, adrenaline flowing) which enables us to either fight the danger or run away.

Despite changes in society our instinctive response to difficult situations is still either to fight (aggressive behaviour) or run away (passive behaviour).

While fighting or running away might have been good tactics in the Stone Age they aren't necessarily the most effective way to deal with situations in the 20th Century! However, it does explain why people don't seem to need courses on aggressive or passive behaviour – it just comes naturally!

It's also worth remembering that the root cause of aggressive and passive behaviour is fear or lack of self-confidence. So most of us are capable of swinging dramatically from one end of the scale to the other, for seemingly trivial reasons.

Building up notches

Ever had days when everything seems to go wrong? Su Lin copes with this by keeping her head down and keeping out of everyone's way. She may have days, months or even years like this, going home with resentment and frustration, until something snaps. She then swings into her aggressive mode. She may lose her temper over something quite trivial, and everyone is astounded, because she's never said anything before!

Every time you ignore a situation or choose not to deal with it and feel bad about it, it builds up a 'notch' of anger and resentment inside. Eventually, like Su Lin, you can get to the point where you blow up.

How do you feel immediately you blow up?

And how do you feel a bit later?

Most people feel great at the time and then guilty or ashamed not long after. The danger is that if you feel so guilty later that you feel bad about yourself, you may decide to keep quiet, and build up more notches; you then find yourself in a vicious circle of passive and aggressive behaviour.

Don't forget you can allow yourself NOT to be assertive too! If you know you can choose to be assertive, you can equally choose NOT to assert yourself on any occasion. You may just not feel up to it that day, or you may decide it's not appropriate. You may still choose sometimes to be aggressive or passive because it seems the best short-term solution, but generally these behaviours won't build good long-term relationships.

How to be assertive

There are no set phrases, trick techniques, or magic words in assertiveness. There are five vital ingredients in any assertive process:

1 **LISTEN**

2 **DEMONSTRATE THAT YOU UNDERSTAND THE OTHER PERSON**

3 **SAY WHAT YOU THINK AND FEEL**

4 **SAY SPECIFICALLY WHAT YOU WANT TO HAPPEN**

5 **CONSIDER THE CONSEQUENCES FOR YOURSELF AND OTHERS OF ANY JOINT SOLUTIONS**

1 Listen

People who are successful at being assertive are good listeners. You may be able to listen well in some circumstances but listening gets more difficult the more complex or controversial the subject matter is. Assertiveness is often about ironing out tricky situations, so listening is a key skill.

2 Demonstrate understanding

Have you experienced someone saying to you – 'I understand how you feel, however, ...' and you are quite certain they *don't* understand! True assertiveness is not a set of trick phrases! In true assertiveness you need to demonstrate, by how you listen and by what you say that you really have understood.

For example: 'You seem very angry and disappointed ...'

This gives the other person a chance to agree that you've got it right or correct it if you have it wrong.

For example: 'Disappointed – yes – but not really angry, more irritated because I've spoken about the same thing several times before.'

3 Say what you think and feel

Take responsibility for your feelings.

Be clear about what has given rise to your strong feelings and attribute them to the event or the behaviour – not the person.

For example: 'I feel really disappointed that you haven't helped around the house in the way you said you would.'

4 Say specifically what you want to happen

Dropping hints doesn't always work! Being clear about what you want to happen increases the possibility of getting it and minimises the chances of being misunderstood. Of course it doesn't guarantee that you get what you want; you have to be prepared for the other person to say no or have a different point of view. Listen to the response you get.

5 Joint solutions and the consequences

Where there is a gap between what you want and what others want, you need to work out a joint solution. Note: Joint solution not compromise. Compromise means that neither of you get what you want. Joint solution means that both of you are satisfied. In exploring joint solutions consider the consequences of each choice on yourself and the others concerned.

How are you doing?

If you're still not sure whether you're behaving assertively or not, check your feelings about yourself and the other person. Remember that assertiveness is about feeling good about yourself. A useful shorthand way of looking at this is as follows:

ASSERTIVE	AGGRESSIVE
I'M OK YOU'RE OK	I'M OK YOU'RE NOT OK
PASSIVE	DEPRESSIVE
I'M NOT OK YOU'RE OK	I'M NOT OK YOU'RE NOT OK

Adapted from Thomas Harris's book, *I'm OK, You're OK* published by Pan.

Listening

Listening is the first key ingredient in an assertive conversation. There is little hope of starting your part of the conversation by demonstrating your understanding if you haven't really taken in what is being said.

It is very difficult to listen to everything that someone is saying, particularly if:

— the other person is waffling
— you disagree with it
— the other person is expressing very strong feelings
— you experience the other's behaviour as aggressive
— there are distractions
— your mind wanders to other things
— you are busy thinking about what you are going to say

Mostly, we can spot when someone isn't listening to us.

What are the signs that you notice when someone switches off?

no eye contact
fidgeting

How do you feel when you're not being listened to?

anger — *'How dare she not listen to me!'*
inadequacy — *'I must be boring her'*

Not being listened to tends to create negative feelings. Keep your listening active to stop these feelings building up.

PEOPLE CAN USUALLY SPOT IF YOU ARE NOT LISTENING

Active listening

Listening well to someone takes a special active effort. It involves:

— quietening yourself down inside
— keeping distractions to a minimum
— paying attention even when you disagree or have strong feelings
— asking questions for clarification
— being open to hear the other person's thoughts, ideas, feelings and intentions
— demonstrating, as well as saying, that you have understood
— giving someone else the space to speak
— being objective about dealing with what you hear

Practise active listening.

Finding the right words

Assertive behaviour involves demonstrating understanding, saying what you think and feel, saying specifically what you want to happen, and working out joint solutions. This means – finding the right words.

The use of words gives clues about the behaviour.

You are having trouble getting started on a piece of work which is usually routine. You say to a passing colleague:

Passive: 'Silly me, I'm getting nowhere with this. My brain must be going.'

Aggressive: 'I don't know whose stupid idea it was to say this had to be done this way. I always said this company was run by idiots!'

Assertive: 'Tracy, I know you're too busy right now, but I'm feeling really stuck on this and could do with some help. When can you spare me ten minutes today?'

Think about yourself and other people around you, and add to the list of typical words and phrases.

AGGRESSIVE	ASSERTIVE	PASSIVE
You ought to … *I'm telling you*	*What do you think?* *I'd prefer to …*	*I hope you don't mind but …* *er, um, ah*

Using words assertively — beginnings

Very often you have to initiate a conversation. In these cases, you can't initially listen as nothing has been said! Your opening remarks still need to:

— **demonstrate that you understand**
— **say what you think and feel**
— **say specifically what you want to happen**

Write down an assertive approach to these situations:

You regularly come up with good information for your boss's boss. Your boss has just rewritten your list in his/her handwriting and pretended it is his/her own. You're very upset about this. You say to her/him:

A colleague has volunteered your help to a department which is overstretched. You are already very busy and are furious that your colleague should make an assumption. You say to your colleague:

Attending a course means you will get home late. You need to ask your partner to collect the children from school and take care of them until you get home. You say:

Now try one of your own situations from page 147 here.

Your situation:

Your beginning:

Using words assertively — replying

On other occasions you have to respond to someone else. You will need to:

— **listen**
— **demonstrate that you understand**
— **say what you think and feel**
— **say specifically what you want to happen**

Using the ingredients, write down an assertive response to these scenarios:

You are doing some DIY at home with a friend when you make a mistake. Your friend loses her/his temper and starts swearing at you and blaming you for other mistakes that have been made. You say to your friend:

You are keen to take on a new piece of work which will widen your experience and involve you staying later in the evening. Although you have volunteered for the work, your manager says: 'Well of course you won't be able to cope with this because you have to get home to look after your kids/mother/dog.' You reply:

You are applying for a job three grades above your current one and ask your manager to support your application. She/he laughs and says 'What on earth are you doing applying for that?' You reply:

Try to avoid using set phrases. Build up some new choices for assertive replies to situations that bother you. Try out one of your own situations from page 147.

Your situation:

Your reply:

Tone of voice and body language

Increasing the assertive words and phrases in your conversation is vital, but the right words on their own will not convey an assertive message. This part of this section is about the two complementary aspects of communication; tone of voice and body language.

The communication researcher, Professor Albert Mehrabian, discovered that the messages that people receive about other people are constituted like this:

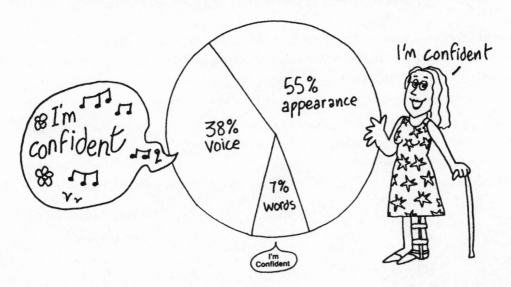

If you are surprised or unconvinced by these statistics, consider the huge number of ways you can convey different meanings with a single word, such as 'really', just by changing the volume, pitch, speed and emphasis of your voice.

So it is hardly surprising that the voice itself is more than five times more important than the words being spoken. For example: Sarcasm only works if the message sent out by the voice and body over-rule the actual words being said.

Think about what you hear around you and compile your own examples of aggressive, passive and assertive uses of voice:

AGGRESSIVE	ASSERTIVE	PASSIVE
loud *clipped*	*steady* *clear*	*soft* *fades out at the end of sentences*

WORDS, VOICE, AND APPEARANCE NEED TO DELIVER THE SAME MESSAGE

If someone is having a conversation with you on the phone then they will have to base their judgement of your message purely on your words and voice. If they can see you, 55% of your message is in what you look like. Your assertive message will be misunderstood if you shuffle your feet, look out of the window or fiddle with your watchstrap. So it's vital to match the body language with the verbal message.

Body language varies from country to country, depending on the culture, so body language has to be read in conjunction with the other signals. It is dangerous to make judgements from one gesture alone. For example, folding arms may be seen as a shutting off, aggressive gesture. It may also be that the person is cold!

We are all experts in body language. Consciously and unconsciously we read it all day. We know when someone is putting out a mixed message, when the words don't agree with the body language.

> With a friend or colleague discuss what you know about the body language used when people are being aggressive, assertive and passive.

AGGRESSIVE	ASSERTIVE	PASSIVE
staring *wagging finger*	*stands upright* *relaxed eye contact*	*nervous smile* *hand over mouth*

> OBSERVE — How people sit in the bus, in waiting rooms, at work, and speculate on what you would read from their posture.

> TRY OUT — The next time you are with a group of people, sit in a way that you think is assertive for a while – see how it feels and if it matches your words.

YOU ARE ALREADY AN EXPERT IN BODY LANGUAGE

Body space

Another aspect of body language concerns the space we give ourselves and others.

Imagine you are travelling home late at night on a train. You are the only person in the carriage until one other passenger boards and sits right next to you, without saying a word or being threatening in any way. How do you feel?

Most of us feel extremely nervous and frightened in that situation. The stranger has become aggressive simply by invading our own personal space.

In day-to-day terms we feel comfortable with some people really close to us and with others we would rather they kept their distance! In his book *Body Language*, Allan Pease describes these spaces as zones. These zones are 'portable air bubbles' that we each have around us.

Zone distances

The sizes of the zones are determined by the culture we've grown up in. For example, while some people are comfortable with crowding, other people are used to wide open spaces and prefer to keep their distance.

The radius of the air bubble around us can be broken down into four distinct zone distances:

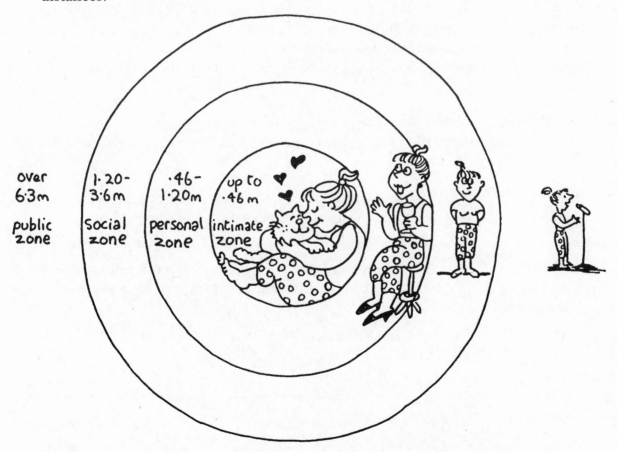

These zone distances tend to apply to people brought up in Australia, New Zealand, the UK, North America and Canada.

Intimate Zone 15 – 45cm or 6 – 18in

Of all the zone distances this is by far the most important as it is this zone that a person guards as if it were her own property. Only those who are emotionally close to that person are permitted to enter it. This includes lovers, parents, partner, children, close friends and relatives. There is also a sub-zone that extends up to 15 centimetres (6 inches) from the body which implies physical contact. This is the close intimate zone.

Personal Zone 46cm – 1.22m or 18 – 48in

This is the distance that we stand from others at parties, social functions and friendly gatherings.

Social Zone 1.22 – 3.6m or 4 – 12ft

We stand at this distance from strangers, the plumber or carpenter doing repairs, the postman, the shopkeeper, new employees at work and people whom we do not know very well.

Public Zone over 3.6m or 12ft

Whenever we address a large group of people, this is the comfortable distance at which we choose to stand.

Being aware of the zones doesn't mean moving around with a tape measure around your waist, but simply to be more aware of the effect of distance.

You may feel that some people stand too close to you – or don't come close enough! You may have found yourself edging down the corridor because the person you are talking to keeps coming too close, or going up close to some people and seeing them backing off.

People coming too close to you or touching you in an unwelcome way may constitute harassment. Find out if your employer has a harassment policy and decide what you want to do about it.

If you wish people to react to you in a friendly, open way, then be sensitive to invading their space – it may be interpreted as aggressive and threatening.

OBSERVE — How close do you stand to other people? Is it comfortable for you? How do you think it is for them? Make notes here about any changes you would like to make:

Interesting how easily men own the space around them, while women just feel like visitors without a permit.

Sarah Dunant – *Fatlands*

Have a go!

Turn back to page 147 and your own real situations.

Have a go at using assertiveness. Tackle your No 1. If there isn't an appropriate moment for it then pick any of your lower numbered situations – start small:

— have a go at something which doesn't matter too much to you.

— recap the main points on pages 149 and 150 and see how you get on.

— review your use of the five ingredient process

— record what happens below:

SITUATION:

I INTENDED TO:

WHAT ACTUALLY HAPPENED WAS:

LOOKING BACK, ONE THING I WOULD DO DIFFERENTLY IS:

LOOKING BACK, ONE THING I'M PROUD OF IS:

MY FEELINGS ABOUT THE WAY I HANDLED IT ARE:

Optional activity – practise with friends or colleagues.

One way to build up your skills is to practise with other people who are familiar with this way of working with assertiveness. Team up with someone who is willing to work with the five ingredients, practise acting out the situations and give each other feedback.

Summary and action

In this section you have clarified the definition of assertiveness, practised some assertive responses and beginnings to situations. You have also prioritised situations in which you wish to be more assertive.

Your personal resource bank

Turn to your personal resource bank and enter the situations in which you now feel you can be truly assertive.

Further optional reading

New books and articles are being produced on assertiveness in increasing numbers. Add the ones you've spotted to this list and decide which to read. Good ones to start with are:

Trades Union Congress – *Sexual Harassment at Work* – published by the TUC
Anne Dickson – *A Woman in your own Right* – published by Quartet
Allan Pease – *Body Language* – published by Sheldon Press

Action

What actions will you take now to be more assertive?

— practise saying no when you mean no.
— get feedback from people close to you about how you come across. Share the definitions first because sometimes people tell a woman that she is very assertive when she is actually behaving aggressively!
— celebrate the success you've had with your own situations.
— decide which of your own assertiveness situations you will deal with next and jot them down here:

I will _____ by_____

I will _____ by_____

I will _____ by_____

I will _____ by_____

Profile

Mary Nelson

I drifted through grammar school, leaving at 16 with few 'O' levels, a love of literature and art and dreams of being an air hostess or model. In reality, life was a 9 to 5 office job, and night school for typing and shorthand. I meandered on, vaguely dissatisfied until a friend arrived back from an ocean cruise. He regaled us with vivid descriptions of people and places and lively anecdotes of life aboard. I couldn't wait. I obtained job descriptions of all available posts – only to discover I was qualified for none. Undaunted, I looked again. Deciding that the title 'Nursing Sister' sounded quite glamorous. I applied to local hospitals to commence student nurse training.

I was accepted. After a shattering first six months, the glamour had disappeared, but I no longer needed my dreams – I had found what I wanted to do. I completed my three years general training, a further year to obtain my Midwifery certificate then on to being the 'perfect' staff nurse. One year later I was offered promotion to sister.

I stopped to reflect. I felt trapped, unready for responsibility and aware how unbalanced my life had become – 'all work and no play'. So I began job hunting and found a post within a large, lively publishing company, combining my nursing and office skills. I met my 'ideal man' – he was ambitious – I was happy. Two years later I had twins. A year later he left – I was devastated.

Almost overwhelmed with feelings of failure, loss, guilt and isolated – I cried a lot. Realising that I needed help I rang the Health Centre. My GP did not offer anti-depressants, he gave me a job as his receptionist. The health visitor's advice was invaluable – take one day at a time and list all your problems, tackle them later. With their continued support I learnt to utilise resources, ask for and accept help.

Learning point: Learn to accept and ask for, help and support.

Local newspapers informed re social outlets, for example; art and pottery classes, museums and parks. The library gave talks, lent books, pictures and records. The Health Centre provided friends and contacts. My elderly neighbours were happy to babysit and introduced me to their Salvation Army Captain. Within a short time I was assisting at the 'Over – 65's' lunch club, teaching brownies and guides. More importantly, he became my friend and mentor for many years.

As my daughters approached 5 I found the best primary school. It was oversubscribed and out of my catchment area, but I secured an interview. Scrubbed and polished, my homework done, the three of us arrived. On my displaying a keen interest in education my children were accepted and I was offered a post as a teacher's aid. I remained there for five years as my daughters neared secondary school age, and began to look to my future. I studied my nursing books, regularly read current nursing magazines and watched for job opportunities in the press.

Learning point: Do your homework. Keep up with current practice.

Our local hospital advertised for staff nurses for their elderly care wards. Explaining that I was 40 and had not nursed for over ten years, I enquired whether they did 'back to nursing courses'. They did not but an interview was arranged and within a month, with no further preparation, I donned my staff nurse uniform once again. Feeling inadequate, but determined to succeed, I gave myself six months to settle or quit.

Learning point: Set yourself targets with measurable dates on.

Many compromises had to be made by both my daughters and myself. Cooking and housework became ad hoc. My bedside note pad was much in use. Neighbours remained supportive as were several friends. Over the next three years I gradually gained in confidence, constantly updating through short courses and regular reading. I felt ready to apply for a sister's post. The interview was a disaster. For two demoralising weeks I kept my head down, then went to my managers for guidance. I was advised to research management literature, talk to the Nurse tutor, shadow a dynamic ward sister and attend mock interviews. Six months later I reapplied and was accepted.

Learning point: Always seek feedback after an interview. It can give you valuable information and advice.

I was a ward sister for five years, responsible for 21 patients and a team of nurses. I sought help when required and continued to research and attend courses including a first line management course. By the end of five years, I knew that I was both physically and mentally tired and needed a change.

Learning point: Don't stay in a job too long. Know when to move on.

I was offered a sideways move into nursing administration as 'Support Sister'. I carved my own niche. I identified areas requiring updating and improvement, did the research and set up workshops to implement new practices and methods, volunteered for committee work and became the link between ward based staff and senior managers.

At the end of one year I approached my senior managers for an advanced grade. I was requested to compile a job description and attend for interview. With the advanced grade I now became 'Clinical Nurse Advisor'. I was now in a position to follow up much of my previous work and was also able to initiate and support innovative practice by teaching and co-ordinating various committees. So followed a very rewarding two years.

I was, however, less well and when reorganisation changes occurred offering early retirement, I took up the option.

A new life now begins. Having not always balanced my social and work life before, I am now planning with care. I have commenced an Access course in English Literature and, if successful, will start a BA degree course next year.

I have time for neighbours, relatives and many ex-colleagues who keep in contact and have also started to draw and paint again. My greatest joy remains the support and affection of my daughters, who despite busy professional careers and full social lives, still visit frequently.

USING ASSERTIVENESS POSITIVELY   9

This above all: to thine own self be true
And it must follow, as the night the day,
Thou canst not then be false to any man. (or woman!)

Shakespeare, *Hamlet*

Objective: To put assertiveness skills into practice in a wide variety of situations

This section is important because:

— assertiveness is easy in theory, but difficult in practice
— the basic ingredients can be adapted to fit different circumstances

Contents:

— using assertiveness when you:
  – are asked for straight information
  – find inconsistency in someone's behaviour
  – need a response from someone
  – aren't being listened to, or aren't being taken notice of
  – are dealing with someone's strong feelings
  – have strong feelings yourself
  – want to say no
  – need to give and receive criticism
  – need to give or receive a compliment
— being assertive with yourself
— summary and action
— profile of Paulette Bushay

Using assertiveness when you are asked for straight information

It hardly seems necessary to learn assertiveness in order to reply to a straight question, but many people tie themselves in verbal knots to avoid giving straight answers to straight questions.

For example: 'What time is the meeting on Tuesday?'

Passive: 'Umm – I think it might be 3 o'clock, but then I'm not sure. You'd better check with someone else. Sorry.'

Aggressive: 'You mean you don't know? You were there when it was organised. Why don't you get yourself together?'

Assertive: '3 o'clock.'

Your assertive replies

Write down your assertive reply to these questions:

'Who's going to make the tea?'   *I made it last time.*

'When will you have that report ready for me?'   *As soon as I can*

'How do you feel about this Springboard workbook right now?'
Surprised how deeply it goes.

Using assertiveness when you find inconsistency in someone's behaviour

An inconsistency may be:

— when someone says one thing and does another
— when someone contradicts something they've already said
— when the printed policy says one thing and the accepted practice is another
— when someone says one thing and looks as if they mean another

The assertive response is not to demand that everything is consistent in life, but to:

— point out the inconsistency
— express the effect of the inconsistency on you
— say what you want to happen

For example: 'You said I didn't have enough experience so I didn't apply for the promotion. Now it's been given to someone with less experience than me. I'm very confused and annoyed about this, and I would like an explanation.'

Your assertive response

Write an assertive response to these inconsistencies:

Your partner has been extremely supportive of you and your career, but has recently started making sarcastic remarks when you work on your revision for your exams. *I find your remarks out of character & would appreciate an explanation of why you are no longer supporting me*

At your manager's suggestion, you have organised a day out to visit other parts of your current organisation and are keen to go. Your manager now says you can't go because of work pressure.

I feel one day visiting other department will broaden my perspective & may through up suggestions of how I can speed up work here.

Using assertiveness when you need a response from someone

When someone uses passive behaviour, it can be difficult to discover what their thoughts and feelings are. Either they do not know themselves or they have decided that it is not relevant or appropriate to express them.

Alternatively, someone may be indirectly aggressive and be choosing not to speak. You may prefer them to voice their opinion on a subject at the time, so you know where you stand and can avoid them saying afterwards: 'Well of course, I never actually agreed with that decision.'

The assertive approach is to make very specific requests to individuals.

For example: 'Well, we've aired the subject of the new computers at length. I'm pretty clear about where Gina, Tom and Andrea stand. Des, I'd like to hear your views on this.'

Your assertive response

Write down how you would find out:

How your partner feels about going to your family again for Christmas.

I'd like to hear your views on where we spent Christmas with you

What's wrong with a friend who has been very quiet since you were promoted over her.

I dont know.

Using assertiveness when you aren't being listened to, or aren't being taken notice of

When you suspect you aren't being listened to the tendency is to move towards either aggressive or passive behaviour. An assertive way of dealing with this is simply to repeat the essential parts of your message, while continuing to acknowledge the other person. You may have to persevere for some time; beware of being sidetracked.

For example: Your Manager and you are about to go to a meeting and she/he is hassling you to get to the meeting on time.

Manager: 'Come on, we'll be late for the meeting.'

You: 'We've got ten minutes yet, I'll be ready.'

Manager: 'We'd better get going now.'

You: 'I'll be ready within 10 minutes.'

Making sure you're heard

Work out an assertive way of ensuring that you are heard in these situations:

You are at a meeting where it is assumed that you will stay until 6 pm. You need to leave at 5 pm to collect your children from the child minder.

I have another appoint want at — & must leave at 5pm

You are explaining to your friend that you do not want her to assume that you will always go out with her on Thursday nights.

I would appreciate the opportunity to plan other to go out on different nights rather than always Its no longer convenient for me to see you every Thursday. I need to deal with other issues

Using assertiveness when you're dealing with someone's strong feelings

One of the vital ingredients in assertiveness is to demonstrate your understanding of the other person. When you feel that a situation is particularly sensitive, and feelings are running strongly, it is even more important to truly demonstrate your understanding. This doesn't mean you have to agree with the other person, but demonstrating your understanding keeps communication going.

Anger is for many the most difficult emotion to deal with. When people are very angry they often don't say 'I'm very angry' or 'I'm furious', but it is obvious from their tone and appearance. Acknowledging the feeling often diffuses it.

For example: You think your mother is angry about something because she keeps snapping at you.

You: 'You seem angry or upset. What's the matter?'

Your assertive response

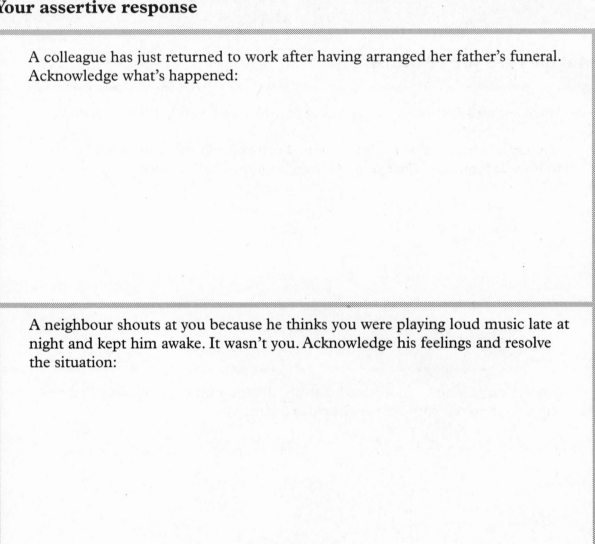

A colleague has just returned to work after having arranged her father's funeral. Acknowledge what's happened:

A neighbour shouts at you because he thinks you were playing loud music late at night and kept him awake. It wasn't you. Acknowledge his feelings and resolve the situation:

Using assertiveness when you have strong feelings yourself

It isn't always possible to think of something positive to say in every situation. Sometimes all you're left with are negative feelings and wishing things were different. In these circumstances, say so. It is important to:

— be very specific
— describe the behaviour that you find upsetting, rather than having a go at the person
— say how this affects you
— say what you would like to happen next

For example: 'When you drive this close to the car in front, I feel very nervous. Could you leave a bit more space?'

Express your feelings assertively

Write your response, saying how you feel and what you would like to happen:

Your friend is flicking through magazines and saying 'mmmm' while you're trying to say something really important to her.

I can see you not interested right now. ~~How can you~~ you ~~give me something~~ this is important - ask for a schedule

You have been working very hard to organise a staff meeting on nursery facilities, which you were very keen to attend. Your boss now tells you that she thinks there is no reason for you to attend the meeting and wants you to answer the phones while everyone else goes.

This is a key issue for me. I suggest we use voice mail for the meeting

Using assertiveness when you want to say 'no'

'No' is one of the shortest but most difficult words for most of us to say.

> Write down why you have difficulty saying 'no':
>
> *I do not have to have every one thinking well of me. As long as I think well of my self.*

No wonder saying 'yes' is easier, even when you'd prefer to say 'no'!

Assertive behaviour means saying 'no' and backing it up with an explanation if you wish. It does not mean making excuses or apologies. It does not mean justifying yourself, ie: going on and on giving excuses (sometimes not even true ones!) so that the other person will think well of you or at least think your reasons are good enough.

For example: 'Could you give me a lift to the station?'

Passive: 'I'm sorry – I can't. I would if I could, but tonight I've got to be at the other end of town to pick my sister up, and the traffic might be bad and I don't want to upset her by being late again. I'm ever so sorry.'

Aggressive: 'Not likely. No way. Why should I?'

Assertive: 'No' plus an assertive explanation if you wish, ie: 'No, I'm picking my sister up tonight.'

Observe how people say 'no'

> Over the next two days listen to yourself, and other people saying 'no' and make notes on how people do it well.

Using assertiveness when you need to give criticism

As with saying 'no', many people avoid criticism as it can be uncomfortable and negative. Giving criticism assertively gives opportunities for change to happen, and often clears the air.

There are 5 steps in giving criticism assertively:

1   Give specific examples of the behaviour you're criticising

2   Say how you feel about the effect it has on you

3   Say what changes you'd prefer to see

4   Listen to the response (words, voice and body language)

5   Work out a joint solution, (not a compromise) to take you into the future – don't get bogged down in what has happened

For example: You overhear a colleague making a sarcastic remark about another colleague.

You: 'When you talk about Angela like that I feel really angry. I don't like the implication that she's slow on the uptake and I'd rather you didn't talk about her like that.'

Give some criticism

Think of a real situation where you would like to give criticism in order to bring about a change.

Write it down, then try it out:

Using assertiveness when you need to receive criticism

Remaining open to receive criticism takes courage. It is one of the ways you have of finding out the effect you have on other people and enables you to decide whether you want to change your behaviour or not. Do not fall into the trap of feeling you have to justify yourself.

There are 4 steps:

1 Remain open – listen to what is being said and ask for specific examples to clarify your own understanding
2 Let the other person know you've heard and understood the criticism, by giving the other person your immediate response
3 Take time to decide: is it all true, is is partly true, is it totally false, what do you want to do?
4 Change your behaviour if you want to

For example: 'I can't see that my not speaking up at meetings could be interpreted as my not being interested. I'm not sure how I feel about that at the moment, and will give it some thought.'

Practise 'criticism situations'

If you are working through this Workbook with other women, get together with two of them to practise giving and receiving criticism, and to do the exercise on the next page. If you are working through it on your own, see who among your family/friends/colleagues will be prepared to read the sections on assertiveness and join you in practising:

Practising has 4 steps:
— Person one describes the scene and the characters briefly and in the practice tries to assert herself.
— Person Two plays the other person; behaving as briefed by Person One.
— If there is a third person, ask them to observe the practice and be ready to give feedback.
— After the practice, participants and observers discuss what they have seen and heard and make constructive suggestions. You may then want to have another go!

Try practising:
— giving criticism
— receiving criticism
— observing and giving feedback

What did you learn? Make notes on the next page, and have a go at compliments.

BEING OPEN TO CRITICISM ENABLES YOU TO GROW

Using assertiveness when you need to give or receive a compliment

We live in a culture where compliments are regarded with great suspicion. Giving them and receiving them is difficult, as people may either think that you're 'crawling' to them or that you have an ulterior motive. Giving and receiving feedback, including compliments, is an important aspect of assertiveness.

Receiving compliments well boosts your self-esteem. People with less self-esteem tend to discount all compliments. Make sure you listen to the ones that come your way.

To give a compliment – keep it short and to the point. Then shut up!

To receive a compliment – keep it short and don't push it away or run yourself down. You may also want to say how you feel.

For example: Receiving a compliment:

'You made a really good job of that piece of work.'

Passive: 'Oh it wasn't particularly difficult – John did most of it anyway.'

Aggressive: (sarcastic) 'Oh you noticed, did you?'

Assertive: 'Thanks. I was pleased with it too.'

Giving and receiving real compliments

Practise giving and receiving compliments with two friends or colleagues.

— Person One gives real compliments for one minute to –

— Person Two who listens, stays open and accepts them

— Person Three observes how the other two get on, then gives feedback

Then swap roles until everyone has had a turn in the three roles.
Make a note of what you learnt from practising giving and receiving criticism and compliments:

Your agenda for action

Write down situations in which you want to be more assertive. Choose whichever of the following categories are relevant to you:

Giving straight information

Inconsistency in someone's behaviour

Getting a response from someone

When you aren't being listened to or being taken notice of

When you are dealing with other people's strong feelings

When you have strong feelings yourself

When you want to say 'no'

When you need to give criticism

When you need to receive criticism

When you need to give or receive a compliment

Tackle three of these over the next two weeks

Being assertive with yourself

Difficulties with assertiveness often start before we open our mouths, as the most difficult relationship to handle is the relationship we have with ourselves. This sets the scene for our relationships with other people.

Being assertive with yourself:

— stops you under-rating yourself

— identifies what you really need

— makes you more productive

— lets you know what you're good at

— helps your actions follow your intentions

The conversations we have with ourselves have a huge effect on the outcomes of situations. They usually become self-fulfilling prophecies, so if you're feeling anxious and sceptical about something, it is likely that you will only 'tune in' to those aspects which fit with your anxiety and scepticism.

In the examples that follow, if the unassertive voices are allowed to rule, the day will be a disaster and the meeting with the friend could end with a row. The assertive voices give a much better chance of success.

UNASSERTIVE VOICE	ASSERTIVE VOICE
'It's Tuesday and it's the departmental meeting. That means everyone's going to be in a bloody mood. It also means I'll be given all sorts of stupid things to do. If that Ian asks me for one more special favour I'll scream! I don't know how I'm going to get through the day.'	'It's Tuesday and it's the departmental meeting – usually a difficult day. I'll deal with each situation as it crops up and practise remaining calm and assertive. I'll say 'no' to Ian if I have no time to do him a favour.'
'I've read all the stuff on assertiveness now, and it seems pretty straightforward. I'll catch Parveen tonight and tell her that I'm not going to her party next week. I'm sure she'll see my point. I'll just give it to her straight.'	'I'll be open and honest with Parveen tonight and discuss with her how I feel about her party next week. It won't necessarily be a comfortable conversation but it's important for me to sort it out.'

How are you getting on with yourself right now? You're nearly at the end of the second section on assertiveness, and you've had a go at practising. What are the voices inside you saying?

'This assertiveness stuff is terribly complicated. I'll never be able to do it' or: 'It's easy, I've got the hang of it now.'

The final aspect of being assertive with yourself involves believing in your own feelings, and really valuing them. This may mean breaking away from your habitual patterns of behaviour, to really explain what's going on inside yourself, and stop making excuses to yourself.

— your assertive self is honest, rational, sane and realistic

— your assertive self is able to assess your own performance realistically and objectively

— your assertive self encourages you

— your assertive self may get shouted down by the other voices

What do the other, non-assertive voices say, to stop you being assertive with yourself?

For example:

Your compassionate friend —	'Her needs are greater than mine.'
Your critic —	'Is that the best you can do? It's terrible.'
Your mouse —	'They'll misunderstand me – I'll just keep quiet.'
Your perfectionist —	'If you can't do it perfectly, then it's not worth even starting.'
Your moaner —	'What can I do? There's no point. Nobody will listen.'

Add some of your own and write down what you are going to say to them the next time they speak up:

VOICE	YOUR POSITIVE RESPONSE

Being assertive with yourself

Think of situations in which you are now going to be more assertive with yourself:

Your assertiveness agenda

Go back to your situations on pages 147 and 174. You've already tried some of them, so tackle another easier one, and work up to your No 10. Aim to have tried most of them, including No 10, by the end of the Workbook. Keep a note on this page of how you got on, so you can learn from your experience.

WHAT HAPPENED	HOW I FEEL ABOUT IT	WHAT TO DO DIFFERENTLY

DON'T WORRY ABOUT GETTING IT PERFECT. HAVE A GO AND ASSERTIVELY REVIEW YOUR ACHIEVEMENTS

Summary and action

In this section you have worked through examples of being assertive in many different situations.

Your personal resource bank

Note the situations in which you now feel you can be truly assertive.

Further optional reading

Ken & Kate Back – *Assertiveness at work* – published by McGraw Hill

Action

What actions will you take now to develop your assertiveness further?

Here are some suggestions:

— tackle some of the many situations that you've noted down
— review progress and don't give up!
— get yourself on an assertiveness workshop. Ask your organisation or check local What's On guide for public courses
— practise accepting compliments well

I will _____ by _____

I will _____ by _____

I will _____ by _____

I will _____ by _____

TAKE THE SMALL STEPS — THE BIG CHANGES WILL THEN TAKE CARE OF THEMSELVES

Profile

Paulette Bushay
Training and Development Manager, Church Army

It was the summer of 1978, the beginning of the end, or so I thought – alone with a couple of CSEs and an 'A' level in Art; this is what the education system and I had achieved in 5 years.

I was born into a working class family, whose traditional stance of men going out to work, women looking after the home was a reality for me. With this kind of conditioning I was convinced that I had already reached my intellectual peak. But I also had a gut feeling that this was not the case. I felt cheated. (I know now that with support and understanding I could have done a lot better) so I was now faced with the decision of a lifetime – take the risk and go to college or find a job. I decided on the latter, at least I could talk to a prospective employer, unlike an examiner.

I very quickly got a job as a trainee Purchase Clerk of a large car company by writing to every local employer who had the first letter of L in the title! (I was convinced that this letter was going to be symbolic). 3 months later I became unemployed. This was due to the fumes of the petrol which led to an asthma attack. When questioned by Personnel why this information was not on my application form, I explained that in my experience, being a woman, being black, and also having an illness, put up more barriers than I could handle.

Learning point: I soon realised that you have to be true to yourself.

At the age of 18 my relationship with my mother was so bad it had become more and more like 'What happened to Baby Jane?' – one of Bette Davies' films. And at the ripe age of 19 I started to head for a nervous breakdown. I was helped by having the positive influence of my first love, the only person apart from my father who expected nothing from me but what I wanted to give.

I decided to move down to London from Nottingham in the early part of the 80s, alone again, but feeling optimistic at a new beginning. I bought a flat and gained employment as a Recruitment Consultant for the banks in the City. This lasted well for 4 years until the company went bankrupt. Yet again I was at the bottom of my career progression route.

Learning point: A crisis can create the space for something new and positive to happen. Use crises positively.

At this point I decided that I had to think what career I was going to pursue. I decided that I would do something over which I had more control, and something where I could have a positive influence in helping others. (AAARGH!)

At this critical stage of my life my father died and I was 7 months pregnant and about to move into my first house. Again I felt alone!

This was the turning point in my life. At 26 years old I decided that I was going to do it my way.

Learning point: Only you can live your life. Make your own decisions.

With the support of friends I became more spiritually aware of myself. This has given me the strength and determination to move forward in anything I choose to.

Learning point: It isn't always important that you come out on top but you come out alive!

I used the same application letters which I had used in my teens to get a job which I wanted this time. I started work as a tutor, then within 6 months became a Manager for a training organisation which concentrates its efforts on the 16–35 age group. I am currently employed as a Training & Development Manager, mainly for 16–24 year olds who like myself feel that either the system, parents, or society has let them down. I know now and understand why I was subjected as a teenager to those 'learning curves' in my life, as that experience is vital for my work now.

I am now fulfilled in my career. I am currently studying for the Institute of Training Management Diploma by distant learning and I am planning to go on to study a Master's degree.

I am constantly balancing the needs of my 5 year old daughter, my partner of 12 years and continuing to do it my way.

Learning point: How to ensure that you will benefit from the development process: Ask for it, give thanks for it, plan for it, believe it is yours now!

MORE ENERGY — LESS ANXIETY

10

Go placidly amid the noise and haste.

Max Ehrmann, *Desiderata*

Objective: To develop healthy ways of dealing with stress and overcoming nerves

This section is important because:

— overcoming nerves saves your energy
— prevention is better than cure
— dealing with small stresses stops them becoming big ones

Contents:

— healthy stress levels
— how do you know when you're stressed?
— making a fresh start
— overcoming nerves
— keep it in balance
— summary and action
— profile of Rosalind Campbell
— food for thought

More energy — less anxiety

Many women are 'multi-committed' — they have considerable family and social, as well as work, commitments. Jobs bring their own particular stresses and strains, whether it's dealing with people, working to tight deadlines, being responsible for work that you really care about, or even having too little to do. Balancing the conflicting demands of a busy life can become a major headache or it can be a dynamic and interesting way of living!

This section gives hints and tips for keeping going, making sure you don't burn out, raising your energy when you need it and remembering to have fun!

The key to more energy and less anxiety is balance. There can be no prescriptions as each person has to find her own point of balance.

Healthy stress levels

Stress is healthy as long as you don't overdo it. Where the level of work and activity in your life is about right you will generally feel OK. Distress results when:

— you're doing the wrong things

— there isn't enough to do

— there's too much to do in the time available

— you regret not having been assertive

— what you have to do is too difficult

— your head tape tells you that you are not doing well enough

— you are creating fight/flight energy and not using it up

Stress symptoms usually creep in unnoticed until we become ill or unhappy. The best way to manage stress levels is to notice them early.

> Try an experiment as you read this. Just freeze your body in the position it is in right this minute. Notice where the tension is in your body, how much pressure you're putting on any one spot. Let go as much of the tension as you can and balance yourself to save pressure or tension on that spot.

> When you are under pressure, where do you usually feel tension in your body?
>
> *Throat, tummy & head.*

One of the toughest aspects of a BBC career is the constant demands it makes on time and energy. This is a critical issue for me, since I'm a single parent with three-year-old twin daughters. It's ironic that, at a stage when I most want to be free to enjoy family life, I'm obliged to make a pretty substantial commitment to the job on which our livelihood depends.

At the same time I'm aware of the need to keep at least a little time for myself — which helps me function better at work, and enriches family life. I regularly make time to swim and take exercise; I like to play music, read books, go to the theatre; and I find space for a wide range of friends.

Caroline Adam
Assistant Head of BBC Radio Scotland

What is the stress level in your life now?

over the top, too much pressure ☑

a bit high, some pressure ☐

comfortable, just right pressure ☐

uncomfortable, too little pressure ☐

What causes you stress now? Not understanding the various stages of my eye changes and treatment

---

What are you already doing about it? Trying to understand it, what to expect etc

---

What do you foresee that may cause you stress in the near future?

My vision becoming weaker. 2 years in the future ∴ 2 years to sort it out

How do you know when you're stressed?

People know they are stressed when they get ill or find themselves in distress, but what about your early warning signals?

Do you experience any of these?

— one or two nights of not sleeping well — YES/NO

— dropping things — YES/NO

— forgetting things — YES/NO

— biting nails, lip or cheek — YES/NO

— wanting more time to yourself — YES/NO

— eating too much/too little — YES/NO

— smoking more — YES/NOT *YET*

— drinking more alcohol — YES/NO

— taking unprescribed drugs — YES/NO *Too stressed to do this*

— feeling sick — YES/NO

— expecting yourself to do more/better — YES/NO

— being irritable — YES/NO

— having minor accidents — YES/NO

— feeling angry, hurt, worried, unhappy — YES/NO

— having aches and pains — YES/NO

— feeling tense — YES/NO

Add anything of your own that you know or think is a symptom of your being stressed:

ALONE NESS

How many symptoms are you experiencing now?

Any one of them needs to be taken seriously but don't be too hard on yourself. If you have more than a couple — consider the root cause of your stress and see what can be done to change it, and find out about the other preventative actions you can take. Most people know a lot about how to prevent stress, but don't actually do enough to put what they know into practice.

The rest of this section gives you:

— ideas about preventative strategies
— hints and tips for short stress relievers
— encouragement to do anything that might help
— an opportunity to start again

Making a fresh start

One simple way to alleviate stress is to try again to put into practice the things that you know or expect will help. Fresh-start days are the ones where you forgive yourself for having failed many times before and try again! Look at:

What you eat and how you eat it *DO THIS*

Make choices about slowly cutting down fats, sugars, binges, fasts, addictions. Increase wholefoods and fresh fruit and vegetables. Take time to eat rather than eating on the run!

Exercise

Find ways to exercise and keep fit that you can enjoy. There's little point in doing exercises that bore you. *DO THIS*

Sports

Which sports interest you? Keep going with ones you already play, take up old ones again and look for new ones to give you enjoyable ways to exercise and get fitter.

Medical and Complementary Health Care

Learn how to talk to practitioners assertively to get the best care for yourself. Find the therapies to suit your ailments and the ones which act as preventatives. Medical research shows that patients recover best when they are treated by a method that they have confidence in.

Pacing

Find the pace of life that you can live at and still find interest and pleasure in each day. Notice how you thrive on the adrenalin of challenges and buckle under the weight of work and relationship overload. Learn how to say 'no' to some requests.

Small steps and visions

Set realistic visions that have a chance of success and then plan small steps in *DO* achieving them. Each small step achieved will give more confidence for the next one. *THIS*

Balance

Find the balance that you need between meeting your needs and the needs of others, the balance of work, relationships and time for yourself. Know when you are deliberately choosing an imbalance, and set boundaries on how long you will allow this to continue. *DO THIS*

Recognising achievements *VERY IMPORTANT   MY OVEN*

Find the positive happening, some would say the 'miracle' in each day, the thing you have done well, or the unexpected event that raised your spirits. Compliment yourself when you have done well, and receive the praise that other people give you.

Allies

Find other people who share your values and can really empathise with your personal, work or relationship goals, and let them encourage you and you encourage them.

Have fun — laughter is the best medicine!

Other positive strategies

There are many stress-reduction ideas and techniques on the market. Find the one or two that suit you and use them regularly over a long period of time to control stress. Local libraries usually have information. Here are just a few examples:

Relaxation — methods of tensing and releasing or talking yourself through letting go. Many types of classes and tapes are available.

Massage — find a qualified practitioner (ie: one with ITEC certificate). Aromatherapy combines massage with the use of healing aromatic oils.

Yoga — several different kinds available — some very gentle and relaxing and some quite energetic.

Tai Chi and other eastern martial arts — give you a series of movements to calm and centre you.

Eurythmy — a series of movements to heal and harmonise your body and spirit and foster the development of your creativity.

The Alexander Technique — a means of using your mind and body together better. Calming, helps posture, breathing and nerves.

Slimnastics — exercise, diet and relaxation.

Meditation — a wide range of techniques and approaches available, both spiritual and non-religious.

Prayer — for those with spiritual or religious beliefs. At its simplest, thinking kindly about another. Many written prayers available from different religious sources.

Counselling — a positive strategy to help you when you need an objective outsider to talk things over with: useful in a crisis, but also very helpful when you need to think things through.

Note any additional strategies you've tried or would like to try:

There are also many short exercises and techniques to help you overcome nerves. The rest of this section gives ideas.

Overcoming nerves

In day-to-day activities people meet sudden attacks of nerves, panic or anxiety. Nerves are normal. Nerves can be overcome or at least minimised. So if, for example, you find yourself getting nervous before an interview, at the beginning of a talk, or in any other day-to-day home or work situation, try some of these exercises.

Each one takes only a couple of minutes. Some of them will be more appropriate to you and your circumstances than others. All of them have cumulative effects. Doing them regularly is like putting money in your calmness bank, which you can then draw on in times of need. Develop your own programme and use the chart on page 191 to keep yourself on track.

The keys to overcoming nerves are:
   breathing, letting go, doing your homework and timing

Breathing

Breathing is automatic — thankfully! But it isn't automatically good! Many people breathe high up in the ribcage and the abdomen doesn't move at all. This means only a small proportion of the air in your lungs is changed and your body loses the energy it might have from a richer supply of oxygen. To improve breathing think about it or work on it for only a minute or two at a time. Don't go on too long or you'll get dizzy!

Two-minute pause
Wherever you are sitting make yourself upright and comfortable and when you've read all the instructions, begin:

— note the time

— close your eyes or just lower them to the ground if you are somewhere too public!

— breathe through your nose, concentrating on breathing out extra, pushing the air out with your tummy muscles. This is better for you than taking in a deep breath

— let your breathing settle again and repeat the longer out-breath three times

— then sit quietly just noticing the breath going in and out over your upper lip until you estimate two minutes have passed

— open your eyes and check the time

The first time you do this, two minutes may seem a long time, or it may have passed quickly. If you haven't done this kind of exercise before it may seem strange or you may feel self-conscious. Do persevere! Practise pausing regularly and you'll get better and better at it and it will calm you down more effectively.

Enhancing your breathing a few times a day balances out, and counteracts, the times you hold your breath or breathe too shallowly. You can also use this exercise before interviews or other nerve-wracking events.

REMEMBER — BREATHE OUT!

Letting go

Letting go is the next step in overcoming nerves. Try three ways:

— **physically**
— **emotionally**
— **mentally**

Physically

Letting go can be achieved by breathing and relaxation techniques, or by exercise. Find out what suits you. If your job is too busy or involves too much travelling to allow you to attend classes, build up the two-minute pause on the previous page to relax your whole body. You can build on it by also doing:

Two-minute release
Start as for the two-minute pause then tell each part of your body to release. Say the word 'release' softly or silently. It's gentle. Repeat it slowly and quietly to yourself while you:

Release your
— head
— face muscles
— jaw and teeth

Let your shoulders drop

Release your
— neck
— shoulders
— arms
— chest
— tummy
— legs
— feet

Go into as much detail as you like. Remember — you may not feel anything happening at first, but keep going to build up the experience.

Palming:
Try 'palming' to let go of the tension around your eyes. Sit at a table. Put your elbows on it and cover your closed eyes with the palms of your hands. After two minutes you'll find you relax more and your vision improves.

Emotionally

Letting go emotionally means reaching the point where your feelings calm down. Firstly, recognise the feeling — and express it, if appropriate. Use your assertive skills to help you resolve situations that trouble you. Secondly, accept the feeling rather than criticise yourself for having it. Thirdly, use the letting go exercise on the next page.

Two-minute letting go

What feeling are you wanting to let go of? Make a clear picture in your mind of the scene or scenes that have given rise to the feeling.

It's helpful if you can select one part of what happened, but it needs to be a significant part — a look on someone's face, a phrase or noise you heard. Make the picture clearly in your mind.

Now erase the picture as you would a video tape and when the thoughts and feelings well up in you again, remind yourself that you are working on it and will keep your thinking about it to the times you set aside.

If you feel you need to digest the situation and the feelings more, set some time aside and contain it rather than allowing the situation to invade the rest of the day. Note any undigested feelings you'd like to work more on here:

If feelings go on being undigested for some time or you feel confused or unsure what to do next, consider having some counselling.

Mentally

Letting go mentally involves controlling your mind, being in charge of the circling thoughts and inner conversations.

Thinking about a problem can be a really useful way of getting to grips with it, but when your mind starts going round and round on a problem and won't let go of it, it becomes stressful, unproductive and energy draining.

Try getting your mind under control.

Why bother? Think of the time that is taken up with scattered thoughts when you need to get on with something. Good time-management means good quality thinking too. Here are three key ways to get your mind under control:

— concentration — to sharpen up your ability to focus on a situation and give it your best attention

— homework — to size up the situation

— containment — to prevent your worry about a situation using up further time and energy

Concentration

Try this two-minute concentration exercise on something totally unimportant. If you practise it regularly every day for a month, you'll find your concentration on more important things improves enormously!

Two-minute concentration

Take a very simple object that comes to hand such as a pen, paper clip, or teaspoon and concentrate on it for two minutes. For the two minutes think about as many aspects as possible of the object.

For example:
— what it is
— where it came from
— what it looks like
— how it is made
— what it is made of
— what it is used for
— what it could be used for

When you find your mind wandering, bring it back to the object. Don't worry if at first you run out of thoughts before the two minutes are up.

Homework

Planning substitutes thinking for worry! Having a plan and doing your homework enables you to contain the worrying. Then you may feel more in control. The main stress factor for many people is worry about the future. This can lead to a string of thoughts that may begin with 'What if ...', eg: What if the train is late? What if they ask me about budgeting? What if she says 'no'?

'What ifs' become energy drainers if they are left unchecked. Instead, use this energy to create positive plans of what you could do.

Think of one event in the future that you are apprehensive about. Pin down one of your 'what if' statements about this event. Then put down every idea you can come up with to deal with it, from the most reasonable to the downright crazy!

What if:	I will:

Now you have your options ready and can either choose your best option now, or leave the decision till the 'what if' actually happens. Very often it won't.

Containment

Next time you find yourself worrying about the event remind yourself that you've already thought about it, and you have a plan ready. Then tell yourself to stop thinking about it.

Containment is a way of disciplining your mind to choose what you think about. It works with practice.

You've tried lots of short exercises to help overcome nerves. Select the ones you are now going to use to build up your calmness bank over the next three weeks. Keep a record of your progress on this chart:

	WEEK 1	WEEK 2	WEEK 3
MON	*palming concentration*		
TUES			
WED			
THURS			
FRI			
SAT			
SUN			

Timing

Choose your timing to suit you.
For example, if you fret and worry when you do things at the last minute, then follow your inclination and do things well before the deadline even if other people think you're silly! Equally, if you work well under pressure, set tight deadlines.

Go with your rhythm

Daily — Are you a morning or an evening person? Plan to do your difficult tasks at the best time for you. On days when you're feeling good, do the things you've been putting off.

Weekly — Is there a pattern? — Are you refreshed on Mondays or do you only really get going by Wednesday?

Monthly — What happens when you've worked solidly for three weeks without a day off? How does your menstrual cycle affect you? How do you cope with weekends being busy as well as weekdays?

Yearly — When do you make new starts, and when do you slump? Is it January, or your birthday, or in September after the summer holidays? Which are your easiest months and which do you struggle through?

Do something when you're not quite ready

Too often we wait till we're pretty sure we can do something perfectly. Stretch yourself. If you always wait till you're absolutely ready, it may be too late.

Remember your 'me time'. Build in some time each day to do something for yourself. It's a great de-stressor.

Keep it in balance

Get the balance right for you. On their death beds, or in old age, people are unlikely to say 'I wish I'd spent more time doing housework' or 'I wish I'd spent more time at the office.' It's more likely to be 'I wish I'd taken more risks' or 'I wish I'd had more time with my family'.

A final note on stress is best said by 87-year-old **Nadine Stair** from Louiseville:

I'd Pick More Daisies

If I had my life to live over, I'd try to make more mistakes next time. I would relax. I would limber up. I would be sillier than I have been this trip. I would be crazier. I would be less hygienic. I would take more chances. I would take more trips. I would climb more mountains, swim more rivers, watch more sunsets ... I would eat more ice-cream and less beans. I would have more actual troubles and fewer imaginary ones. You see, I am one of those people who lives prophylactically and sanely and sensibly, hour after hour, day after day. Oh, I have had my moments and, if I had to do it all over again, I'd have more of them. In fact I'd try to have nothing else. Just moments, one after another, instead of living so many years ahead each day. I have been one of those people who never goes anywhere without a thermometer, a hot water bottle, a gargle, a raincoat, and a parachute. If I had it to do over again, I would go places and do things and travel lighter than I have.

If I had my life to live over, I would start bare-footed earlier in the spring and stay that way later in the fall. I would play hooky more. I wouldn't make such good grades except by accident. I would ride on more merry-go-rounds. I'd pick more daisies.

Summary and action

The message in this section is: be kind to yourself and use your common sense to keep you fit and well emotionally, mentally and physically

Further optional reading

Jacqueline Atkinson — *Coping with stress at work* — published by Thorsons

Leslie Kenton — *Passage to Power* — published by Vermillion

Action

What action are you now going to take to ensure your stress levels stay healthy?

Here are some suggestions:

— pick up again, or do with new enthusiasm, any stress relieving techniques you have used successfully in the past

— learn one of the techniques mentioned on page 186

— use the two-minute exercises to overcome nerves, relax or concentrate

— ask friends about what works for them

— take some 'me' time

I will _____ by _____

I will _____ by _____

I will _____ by _____

I will _____ by _____

Profile

Rosalind Campbell
Science Teacher

I had not planned to go to work after doing my 'A' levels. I wanted to go to Medical School and had my heart set on becoming a doctor. I did badly in my 'A' levels and all my applications to medical school were rejected. It was a difficult time for me – my father had just died and I lost the interest or drive to do anything. In addition, after a life of suffering pain, missing lots of school and going in and out of hospital, the realisation of knowing that I was suffering from an illness which meant that I would not be able to have 'a normal life' went on in my head like a light bulb.

I got a job in the NHS as a Junior Medical Laboratory Science Officer without any difficulty. I was trained to screen cervical smears. The work was interesting for a while but I could see that it would become very routine and terribly boring in the long run. I still wanted to become a doctor, so I left and went to college to study for a science degree as a mature student of 21 years old! The plan was to complete the degree and then go on to get a medical degree, but by the end of the three years I could not face doing any more studying, so I completely dropped the whole idea and went back to work in the NHS.

I stuck my job out for a year during which time I became very bored, so when I saw a job for a laboratory technician in a school advertised, I applied and got the job. It was working in the school that first made me think about going into teaching. I had a degree and I could use my experience as a laboratory technician as evidence of my ability to become a science teacher. Also the regular holidays would be helpful for my health. I did a teaching qualification, and started teaching 6 years ago. After 2 years I was promoted because the way to get ahead was to take on additional responsibility, but my health was suffering. I was under pressure all the time – marking, preparation, writing reports. My social life went out of the window as I had to work every evening. I felt constantly exhausted. The Head teacher and staff were sympathetic to my illness which helped.

At this time, I met Leena, a dynamic, confident, competent Head of Science at a Saturday School in which I teach. I was impressed by her success and her vitality for the job and the children. She told me that I was working too hard for too little money. She encouraged me to look for promotion in another school and spent many hours with me going through how to 'sell myself' applications and interviews.

I was shortlisted for a job and got an interview. I was up against two fairly tall men who had much better degrees. This is where image is important. If you look smart you are judged as being efficient and capable. I talked to the 'opposition' in between the tour of the school and between interviews to seek out their weaknesses. If they lacked experience in certain areas, I would make sure that I emphasised my strengths and experience in those areas. I got the job but they wanted to know about my illness. I had been through this before with other jobs, so I wasn't too concerned about the outcome. When I saw the doctor he, in effect, told me that he could not recommend me for my new job because I would take too much sick leave due to my illness. I was angry and shocked because I was fit enough to teach in another borough, but not this one. I decided that I would go to the Press if I did not get the job, and I spent sleepless nights composing what I would say to reporters. A few days later I got the all clear.

I have been working here for several months now. Although the path to advancement in my career is now open to me, my life is so skewed towards work that I am getting little enjoyment out of it. The prospect of the rest of my life being like this does not fill me with anticipation. Meanwhile, since doing my 'A' levels I have neglected the artistic/musical side of me which was almost my entire life at school.

Now at 34, my personal goal is to build more flexibility into my life so that I have more time to do the things that I enjoy. I am prepared to make sacrifices because although I am deeply interested in science I need to satisfy other aspects of my nature and keep my illness under control. I do not view myself as a failure or accept anything as a failure in my life – it is negative and soul destroying to think like that. Just after my father died, I read a book by Richard Bach called 'Illusions' which speaks of 'problems' as being 'gifts' which we need in order to 'make our lives better' and I live by this. It has helped me to keep on top of an illness which could completely dominate my life and cause me to lead a meagre existence, and it has given me the confidence to continue when I feel like giving up. It has really worked for me. Everybody should have a personal 'philosophy' by which they live.

Learning points:

If you don't enjoy what you are doing, do something else.

If you want something badly enough, seek out the people who are there already and use them to get whatever help you need.

Accept help from others and seek out support.

Do not be afraid of failure – it is just another 'learning' point in your life.

All the money in the world will not make you happy if you have to work like hell for it.

Make time to do things that give you pleasure.

If you have an illness, be positive about it, don't let it consume your life.

Food for thought

Helen Sharman
Britain's first Astronaut

When I heard the advert on the car radio I realised that it was an opportunity that would come only once in my life. Too often we let things go because we think they will not work out. You have got to be prepared to take risks, it is no good just wishing you were doing something else. For goodness sake, you have only got one life, use it, and have fun with it.

Pippa Isbell
Managing Director — PIPR

Dare to do more — stick your neck out, ask for the job or the responsibility; back it up by doing the job well and with careful preparation to reduce the chances of failure. If you should fail, make sure that you do not repeat any mistakes then put it out of your head and move on — guilt is wasted energy.

Become an expert — specialise in something that's important to the department or the company and let everyone know that you have this expertise. Once you've capitalised on the position it creates: move on and learn about something else — don't become indispensable because of the specialism.

Be brave — sticking your neck out is a lonely business. You have to be strong and take heart — it definitely gets easier and better.

Jacqueline Hughes
Branch Executive — The MI Group

Balance between home and work didn't exist before I had my son, especially as I work in the same office as my husband Stephen, but that has had to alter and I love it! Life outside work: I conceived and ran 'The Luncheon Club' for business women for 4 years and am moving on this year to setting up a dining club! Treasurer of NW Industry Matters Women's Group. We produce a Directory of Women in Industry in the NW and put on seminars. Also I am a member of International Food & Wine Society — I love good food and wine!

Why does a large elephant stay tied to a small stake? Because it has been conditioned to believe it can't escape.

Why do bees fly when aerodynamically they shouldn't be able to? Because no-one has ever told them!

The only difference between being in a rut and being dead is 6 feet.

MANAGING YOUR IMAGE

11

Managing your image is not about trying to be something that you are not. It's about becoming aware of all your strengths, and using body language and dress to make the best of them. It's about being yourself and putting the best you forward.

Lee Bryce, *The Influential Woman*

Objective: To achieve the visibility you need to match your values and achieve your goals

This section is important because:

— good performance is not enough
— people need to know what you're doing
— impressions count
— good work needs to be seen to be done

Contents:

— you
— your customers and stakeholders
— your image
— your message
— your job mobility
— your public relations campaign
— your exposure
— so what?
— summary and action
— profile of Smita Patel

Managing your image

The organisational research mentioned on page 33 showed that good performance contributed only 10% to whether people get recognition or promotion. The image people created accounted for 30% and their exposure 60%. Most people are outraged when they hear these figures and see them as confirmation of what an unjust world we live in. We would like to think that the person doing the best work gets rewarded, but stop and think about the reality of the situation. How will people know: –

— you're looking for a new/different job?

— you're doing a good job?

— you're ready for increased responsibility?

— you've extended the range of what you do?

— you exist?

— you're the person to do that special project?

— you're ready for more training?

— you're keen to get on?

On the whole, people at work are not telepathic or lying awake at night worrying about you! They will only know about you, your good work, your ideas and aspirations, if you tell them. So, as well as doing good work, you also need to give consideration to the image you create, and how high your exposure is. That is, how visible you are. This is especially important in a recession when there is a sizable pool of people available, many of whom are already capable of good performance.

Good image lets people see your good performance

Most of us feel better about ourselves when our good performance is being recognised, but recognition only comes when people can see how well you are doing.

So even if your goal is clear to you, your image may prevent others seeing you in ways that match your goals.

For example: By consistently staying late and conscientiously doing extra work Moa thought that she was creating an image which would help her promotion prospects, by demonstrating that she was committed, keen, and hard working. Unfortunately her director interpreted her behaviour as demonstrating that she was overstretched, unable to cope and obviously not ready for promotion.

Personnel specialists often comment on how reluctant women are to think about this aspect of personal development. The idea of building an 'image' may seem to suggest that you become a phoney, a superficial and manipulative person.

This is not true. The image to build is the true one. This means being more yourself and putting the best 'you' forward. People need to have the clearest picture of you so they know who you are, what you want and what you have to offer, so you're going to have to take the initiative, and tell them about you! They won't ask!

If you've been ignoring this aspect, it might explain why:

— you seem to do good interviews but never get the job
— your friends don't take your idea of setting up your own business seriously
— your ideas always get ignored
— you get taken for granted
— you've become a Flossie

Your image is one of those things that is always with you – like your shadow it never goes away, is there for others to see, and is a part of you. Even if you choose to do nothing about it, you will still have an image, because everyone else will still have an impression of what sort of person you are.

The good news is that, unlike your shadow, you can change and adapt your image, so that it supports and reinforces what you're trying to do, rather than contradicts or undermines your efforts.

Image is not just the clothes you wear, it's the whole impression you create every day in all aspects of your life. Find the image that has the right balance for you.

In finding the balance, consider the two extremes open to you:

— at one end of the scale is the person who does not consider her image at all and takes the view that her work alone will gain her the recognition and acknowledgement that she'd like.

— at the opposite end of the scale is the superficial person who is all image and has no solid skills, qualities and experience to back it up. A sham.

So concerned with image that you lose your real self

No concessions to image at all

Image to fit your values and your goals

To find where you feel comfortable in between these two extremes, you will be influenced by your values and your integrity, so it may help to look again at page 56 to clarify your values. It is important that you feel good about the image you project, and that it fits you, your goals and your values.

In essence, be yourself, but be sure to project an image that does you justice and fits with your ambitions.

Janet Cameron, Managing Director, Inglis Office Supplies

The rest of this section gives you opportunities to check your image against your goals and values using an approach which promotes you in ways that you approve of. The approach brings you the visibility you need to get your good performance recognised. It applies to work and personal matters and covers:

You

Before you start promoting your positive image, you need to gather raw material about yourself and how others see you. A great deal of the work that you've done in the workbook so far contributes to this. You may find it useful to ask for further feedback on the impression you create both at home and at work.

Your customers and stakeholders

Customers are people who use your services. For example: managers, colleagues, family, potential employers.

Stakeholders are people whose lives are affected by the things you do and the goals you set. For example: partners, bosses, friends, children.

Each has different needs. Try putting yourself in their shoes, and really understanding what their situation is.

— What are their needs?

— What do they really care about?

— What's in it for them, if they help you?

Photocopy the next page before you write on it and then build up your notes about what your customers and stakeholders really need. Then you can decide whether or not you are in the market to supply it!

Work through at least two examples of people whose needs you are considering meeting – the customers and stakeholders.

Fill out the next page or keep separate notes in a safe place.

Needs File

Name: *Lorna McIntosh*

Position: *Marketing Manager*

Needs: *People with lots of bright ideas who can manage others. Lots of prestige. Needs to be supported in doing things differently. Needs to be promoted soon — she's got stuck.*

Especially rates: *People who make her laugh. People who get on with things by themselves. Experience in Sales.*

Likely attitude: *So-so. She either likes you or not. Patchy record on appointing non-graduates.*

Needs File

Name:

Position:

Needs:

Especially rates:

Likely attitude:

Needs File

Name:

Position:

Needs:

Especially rates:

Likely attitude:

Your image

Research by Professor Albert Mehrabian shows that the ways people receive messages from you fall into 3 categories:

More than half the impression you create is in how you look. This is something we are all very aware of when we are consciously trying to create an impression – most of us wear special clothes to interviews, and dress up for special occasions.

However, people are piecing together their impression of you all the time so, if you want your message to be strengthened, it needs to be consistent.

Imagine walking into a roomful of people who you don't know. You immediately gain an impression of who the central characters are, who are in the supporting roles, and how everyone is feeling. The visual clues are:

— their posture

— whether people look you in the eye

— how expensive/old/new/tidy/untidy their clothes look

— their liveliness

— whether they smile

— the expression on their face

— hairstyle

— how colourful their hair/clothes/make-up are

— accessories, such as ear-rings, glasses, briefcase, etc.

— their mannerisms

It's not enough to have the right clothes, you also have to wear them with style and confidence! But what are the right clothes? Think about your key customers. Do you know what they're looking for?

Power dressing is a controversial subject. In the USA, stories are told of how women there have to wear tailored suits, with immaculately manicured nails and a fresh hairstyle, before their male colleagues will listen to them. Thankfully, Susie Faux, shop owner and wardrobe consultant tells us that *'power dressing is dead in the UK!'*

The clothes code doesn't operate so strictly in Britain, but this doesn't mean that it isn't there – it means that you have to work it out for yourself. A very useful rule-of-thumb is 'dress for what you're aiming at.' A suit and briefcase might be appropriate if you're considering mainstream management, while trendy trousers and top might help your case to get into a design studio. A recent survey showed that most people assumed that a woman wearing a jacket had power and authority.

If you wear a uniform, then you may have little, if any, choice in the actual clothes you wear, in which case all the other aspects of your image become more important.

For example: Morag is a 27-year-old bright, ambitious graduate secretary. She talks about moving onward, sideways, anywhere, but she always gets the same response – an indulgent smile and a shut door. In frustration, she sought feedback, and discovered that people thought she was about 20 and rather unambitious. She also discovered that her long, loose hair, frumpy clothes, and fresh, round face were all contributions to her little girl image.

She resolved to smarten up, had her hair re-styled, and experimented with clothes. A new briefcase replaced her elderly bag, and Morag found that people took her aspirations more seriously and that her new image matches what she thinks about herself.

Judge for yourself:

Do these three things, then rate yourself on the chart on the next page. Get a friend to help if need be:

— look at the contents of your wardrobe – objectively

— look at yourself in the mirror – really look from top to toe – again, objectively

— dig out some old photographs of yourself and see how you've changed

Dress as if you mean business. Coco Chanel once said that if a woman is poorly dressed you notice the clothes, if she's well dressed you notice the woman.

Vikki Worthington
Researcher, Central Independent Television plc

Rate how much help your appearance is giving you towards achieving your goals by ticking the appropriate column:

Aspects of image	Actively holding me back	Making it difficult	Neither one way or another	Getting there	Doing a great job
clothes - tidiness					
- style					
- quality					
- age					
shoes - tidiness					
- style					
- quality					
- age					
hair - style					
- colour					
glasses - style					
accessories					
briefcase					
handbag					
nails					
make-up					
posture					
cleanliness					
smile					
facial expression					
weight					
height					
sparkle in the eyes					
zest and energy					
jewellery					
OVERALL IMPRESSION					

Your message

If you were selling a product you would decide on the message that needs to be put across and then choose the right medium. Section 12 looks into the opportunities to put yourself across in application forms, CV's and the like. The message you put across should:

— **address the needs of your customers and stakeholders**
— **demonstrate the benefits**
— **prove results with evidence**
— **be positive**
— **be memorable**

Address the needs

Show how you can meet the needs you've identified for customers and stakeholders:

Note – you can decide to refuse to meet their needs too!

The needs are:	I can meet them by:
to be supported not challenged	*building on her ideas rather than demolishing them*

Demonstrate the benefits

Very often, people describe themselves solely in terms of what they are. Talking in terms of benefits means adding how these aspects of yourself will benefit the customer and stakeholder.

Write down at least four features of yourself and work out the corresponding benefit:

Feature about me	Benefit to the customer
I am good with people	Less hassle in the department
I have stayed in the same department for the last five years	In-depth knowledge and experience available
I am keen to take on more	He/she will be able to delegate more

Most people do not promote themselves in this way. They support their application for a job, their proposal for a revised holiday rota or whatever, by emphasising how it would help *them*, without considering the effect and potential benefits to those they're trying to influence.

From now on, stop and put yourself in the other person's shoes.

Prove the results with evidence

When products are advertised, the manufacturers always focus on the results you will get from using a particular brand – it washes cleaner, is kinder to hands, and so on! Promote yourself in the same way with the messages you give about you. The more specific and clear you are with the evidence about what you do, the more effective your message will be. Work out at least four examples of real evidence of how good you are:

Feature about me	Prove it with evidence
Open to new ideas	*Learned about computers at 50*

Be positive

Adverts do not point out the things that are unhelpful about a product, or remind us of how the product doesn't work, but people do. It is not unusual to hear people say negative things like: 'This job is boring' rather than: 'I'm ready for more responsibility'

Develop five really good, positive things to say about yourself and be able to back them up with evidence:

1

2

3

4

5

Be memorable!

Things about you that make you different or special in some way also make you more memorable. These things are useful ingredients in your positive message and will:

— make you stand out

— make you preferable to the competition

— be very convincing

— make you better

— make you new

— make you special

— make you different

— make you unique

— make you the best

— make you memorable

Think of one thing about you that makes you memorable:

Your job mobility

When promoting yourself in new ways be clear about how far you would be prepared to move house or travel.

If you're prepared, and able, to go anywhere at any time, that makes you very special, so shout about it! It is one of your big plusses. If, like most people, you aren't able or don't want to go that far, then ensure that the way you describe your mobility is positive, and consistent with the rest of your message.

For example: I really want to work with young people – I'm looking for any opportunities in and around Glasgow.

Your public relations campaign

Free gifts and demonstrations are ways of letting the customer try out the product without paying for it, in the hope that he/she will then want to buy it.

Some organisations offer secondments, job shadowing or attachments between departments – this is an opportunity for you to demonstrate to a possible new customer how great you are, lets them try you out and lets you try them out, day-to-day.

Other ways of demonstrating how great you are, without anyone paying any extra money for you, are:

— volunteering to do things

— getting yourself onto steering groups

— organising social events

— having bright ideas

There is a fine line between this positive PR and being walked all over! Remember that you're doing this to demonstrate your skills and abilities. The moment you feel you're being taken for granted is the moment to review your strategy.

For example: Sharon, 'As a Personnel Officer out in a branch, I was acutely aware of my lack of knowledge of what was going on in head office, so I volunteered to be on a central working party. My contacts have increased, people know me, and I've learnt a lot about how things happen at that level.'

Another part of public relations campaigns is the use of celebrities and existing customers to promote products. This is because people are more convinced by an 'unbiased' view. If you say you're great – that's your advertising, but if someone else says you're great – that's your public relations! It carries more weight and credibility.

Ways of using other people's views of you include the formal – such as referees, to the informal – such as someone else dropping your name into conversations.

For example: Snigda recently attended a course where a more senior manager spoke. In the bar afterwards, she did a good job of explaining about herself and her career aspirations to him. He was impressed and remembered her so that when her name cropped up as a candidate for an internal promotion, he suggested that she be shortlisted – she got the job!

Keep the public relations going by making sure you tell people about the 'new improved you' when you have new skills, qualifications, additional experience or a greater commitment to what you're doing. Widen the scope of your public relations campaign to match your new goals.

Your exposure

No – this isn't about strip-tease! You may remember that on page 33, Harvey Coleman's statistics told you that 60% of whether you get promoted or recognition depends on your exposure, so it's worth thinking about! Exposure means:

— getting yourself known

— getting your name known

— getting your face known

Some ways of doing this are:

— extending your contacts

— keeping up existing contacts

— getting involved in social/sports activities

— organising things

— writing articles for newsletters

— getting yourself in the internal newspaper/news-sheet

— speaking up on courses/at meetings

— being memorable – for whatever reason!

How are people going to remember you? You'll have to tell them that you exist, that you're good, and what you want. And you'll probably have to tell them over and over again. It's a matter of grabbing every opportunity to remind people about you and your work.

For example: Alison was recently asked to give a short talk to another department. Afterwards the organiser sent her a memo congratulating her on her good presentation skills.

Alison sent a photocopy of the memo to her immediate boss and her boss's boss. The memo then went up the line, with each person scribbling a comment on it. By the time the memo came back to Alison, there were six congratulatory comments scribbled on it, and Alison had successfully increased her exposure at a more senior level.

Meetings are another opportunity to make yourself and your views known. However, meetings can be fraught with difficulties and it is all too easy to be overlooked and become invisible. If this tends to happen to you, remember: '**The Mouse at the Meeting**' law.

This says that unless you say something within the first 10 minutes of the meeting, the chances are that you won't say anything at all. Watch the Mouse at the Meeting law at work – there's a lot of truth in it! If you think you may be a mouse at a meeting, make a point of speaking up within those all-important 10 minutes – anything to get yourself heard and noticed and to break the ice. You'll then find it much easier to speak up later on.

Some ideas that have worked for other women are:

— asking for a window to be opened or closed

— asking if there's an agenda

— checking the objective of the meeting

— building on someone else's point

— agreeing with someone else's point

Put yourself across positively

Give a 2-minute positive talk about yourself.

If you're not used to speaking positively about yourself, try practising with a group of family, friends or colleagues, or if that is not possible, talk into a tape recorder and play it back the following day. If others join in, give each other feedback on how positively you come across and where you let yourself down.

This is an opportunity to really blow your own trumpet, so be as outrageous as you like!

Get feedback on:

— what you felt was positive about the way you came across

— what you felt was negative about the way you came across

— where you felt you sold yourself short

— were you being modest?

— were you believable?

— were you over the top?

— what did you learn from or have reinforced by this exercise?

So what?

Having looked at aspects of your image, what do you want to do about it? Nobody goes around thinking of all these things all the time, but rather like assertiveness skills, it is good to have image-building skills available to you for when you need them. Again, like assertiveness skills, it is important to be clear and consistent in your message, or you run the risk of confusing your customers and stakeholders.

All this takes a lot of time and effort, and may seem like a lot of bother. Every campaign needs investment and commitment at the beginning to get it moving. You may now be facing spending money on new clothes or a new haircut, or going to an exercise class.

Take small steps, and persevere. People may laugh the first day you turn up with a new hairstyle, or express yourself positively. Doing things differently may make you vulnerable to jibes and sarcasm, but stick to it. People's memories are very short, and your new way of talking about yourself won't be considered worthy of a joke in a couple of weeks.

In this Section you have considered some of the overall aspects of how you come across to people. Section 12 builds on this with ideas on image-building in specific formal situations.

Summary and action

In this section you've looked at why image-building is important and you've thought about your own image. The image to project is the real you, so that people can really see you and what you can do.

Your personal resource bank

Add your benefits and evidence
Add the things that make you special and/or different

Further optional reading

Eleri Sampson – *The Image Factor* – published by Kogan Page
Diana Mather – *Image works for Women* – published by Thorsons

Action

What action are you now going to take to develop your image?

Here are some suggestions:

— clear out a drawer or wardrobe and dispose of items that don't fit your new image
— make a point of speaking up more at the next meeting that you attend
— let people know about your aspirations
— dress for your goals
— make contacts in a different part of the organisation

I will _____ by _____

I will _____ by _____

I will _____ by _____

I will _____ by _____

Profile

Smita Patel
Negotiator, Business Development, Texaco Limited

I cannot remember ever devising a stringent career plan. Experience has taught me to be flexible with the opportunities that are available to me. My only plan after graduating in Business Studies, was that my 'real job' would be in the discipline that I had studied.

Whilst on a short term assignment with Marplan, a comparatively large and well reputed marketing research organisation, one of the Managing Directors offered me a full time position as an 'International Passenger Survey Executive'. The position had become available as a result of the company's decision to relocate its offices to Central London. The existing staff were unwilling to move with the company.

Learning point: Be prepared to do jobs other people don't want and turn them into opportunities.

The client was a government department which demanded accurate information as well as meeting a stringent deadline during the reshuffle/organisation change. I was made aware when accepting the position that the client had every right to take its contract elsewhere if we did not provide the service and required results. The renewal of the contract each year until I left the company and healthy pay rises gave me the comfort that both the client and my employers were happy with my work and respected the responsibility of my position.

The Managing Director who recruited me had a significant impact on the manner in which I worked then and now. The key elements which I have learned for success in a job are:

- being flexible and adaptable
- being happy in one's work
- having full support from the right people
- being politically astute but not participating in political battles
- to do one's best in the job
- being busy, and plenty of hard work
- to ask for advice when the need arises.

Learning point: Find and learn from good managers.

After a year and a half, the department was functioning extremely smoothly. This to me was the achievement I desired, but it also meant that my role was no longer challenging. Looking around I noticed that most executives had the same clients year in, year out, so I decided that it was time for me to move on to an organisation which could offer me fresh challenges.

Learning point: Do your homework about your own organisation and be aware of what else is available.

I left Marplan politically naïve, as the organisation was predominantly female dominated and I did not come across any prejudices. The company was geared to ensuring business success and the quality of one's work was recognised and played an important part in the organisation.

I then joined an oil company. There were two significant changes that I had to come to terms with. The first one was attitude – I was one of only three 'professional' females on site. The second was the organisation's size. Both I viewed from a positive aspect, and I had to change my attitude too, by becoming more tolerant and less sensitive.

The job was high profile which meant that more people (both internal and external to the organisation) were aware of my work. This meant that I had to work three times as hard to ensure that my output was much better than required. It also meant that I had to spend a lot of my own time researching and learning areas where I lacked technical knowledge. The company itself was good in training and I took the opportunity of in-house training.

Learning point: Know your own organisation and your own strengths and vulnerabilities within it. Take every opportunity for training and learning new skills and knowledge.

As the organisation was large, there were more opportunities to move to fresh challenges. The company then underwent a major restructuring and this resulted in the relocation of its staff. I left to join my existing company, Texaco.

Since joining Texaco, I have worked on major projects and gained higher responsibilities. My work involves dealing with companies in the industry and I am aware that I am representing Texaco at all times. This involves being fully prepared and preserving certain industry etiquettes. The fact that some of the people that I am dealing with are more experienced than me encourages me to 'do my homework'.

Learning point: You never stop learning.

I have had good opportunities so far as a result of certain managers recognising my capabilities and utilising my skills to the full. Texaco is, to my knowledge, one of the few companies which has recognised the challenge to utilise all the skills available within the organisation. Texaco are taking positive steps to ensure that they tap into all skill areas and allow their employees to realise their full career potential. This, of course, helps build business success.

I personally have no strict plans as such. I do not feel that I have attained 'success' – I am still working to that objective.

BLOWING YOUR OWN TRUMPET

12

She who gets hired is not necessarily the one who can do the job best, but the one who knows the most about how to get hired.

Natasha Josefowitz, *Paths to Power*

Objective: To put your own message across effectively

This section is important because:

— your image and exposure contribute to your getting the job
— the application form gets you the interview
— casual conversations can give lasting impressions
— your image is being built every day
— many organisations have an open system of competition

Contents:

— application forms
— curriculum vitae
— covering letters
— interviews
— other formal conversations
— summary and action
— profile of Mary Blance

Blowing your own trumpet

If you want to move yourself on to the next step, the messages you produce need to have a positive effect. A good application form gets you the interview, a good interview gets you the job; the way you put yourself across day-to-day builds your own public relations campaign.

This section is a practical one, full of tips and do's and don'ts. They are all straightforward common sense, but as so often with common sense, it's good to be reminded! It covers the key elements of job applications.

Whether you're applying for something internally or from outside, at some point you'll encounter an application form, be asked for your CV and experience an interview. These are all formal ways of blowing your own trumpet. The important thing is to do just that! Don't be put off by terrifying job descriptions or vague adverts – use all the work you've just done in Section 11 as your raw material and think of job applications as the vehicles for putting it across.

Women are notorious for not applying for jobs because they don't feel they fit all the criteria perfectly. Personnel people tell of how frustrating it is not to be able to promote or appoint women – because they don't apply. The same people also tell of how men tend to adopt the opposite attitude – if you've got one of the requirements mentioned, it's worth a try! Obviously this makes a huge generalisation about women and men, but if in doubt, get out there and have a go! You may not get the first job you apply for, but you'll build up experience in applications and interviews and you could get feedback on how you did.

Applying from inside

If you're applying internally for a regrade, promotion, sideways move, or whatever, you may not be asked to fill in an application form, you may simply be asked to apply in a letter or memo. In this case, it's the only piece of paper that you have to advertise yourself, so give it as much thought and attention as you would a full application form. Equally, if there is an internal application form, ask to see a copy now, so it won't come as a surprise when you come to complete it in reality.

Remember that the people interviewing you internally often do not have access to your file, so your application letter/form is the only document that they have about you – make it gripping reading!

Applying from outside

If you're applying from outside the organisation, then you'll need to do your homework. Here are some suggestions:

— ask for a copy of the annual report, the house magazine and any other useful publications, before you prepare your application.

— research the organisation in the local library – the librarian will help you.

— read the relevant trade/industry magazines and familiarise yourself with current topical issues.

— think of anyone you know who knows someone who works there, or in a similar organisation. Arrange to talk to them about the organisation or business.

— ask for an application form as early as possible, so you can be thinking about the format and learning more about how the organisation works.

— consciously keep your eyes and ears open for information about your prospective employer in the press. Refer back to Section 7 on Getting Information.

— experience the organisation in whatever way that you can, eg. walk through the premises if they are open to the public or buy something as a customer.

Application forms

Tailor each one specifically to the job you are applying for.

Some nuts and bolts

— get it typed or use capitals in an ink that will photocopy easily

— get it checked for spelling and understanding

— make sure the final version looks neat and clean with an easy-to-read layout

— be consistent in the way you present information, ie: starting in the past and moving into the present, or the other way round

— make a photocopy for your interview preparation

— staple any extra pages and the covering letter to the application form – a paper clip isn't enough

Getting your message across

— address the requirements of the job description or advert

— only put information that supports your case

— anticipate what they're looking for and address it head on – refer back to page 205

— be ENTHUSIASTIC

— use every space to tell them what you want to tell them

— make yourself different, eg: instead of 'cooking' as an interest, be more specific – 'French pastry cooking'. Instead of 'reading' – 'the novels of Maeve Binchy' – refer to page 208

— don't be afraid to go on to another sheet of plain paper to get in all the right information. If you've written it well, people will happily read on

— make it results-orientated, not just a recitation of what you are/were responsible for – refer to the bottom of this page

— you can influence the content of your interview by what you put, and don't put, on your application form

— the most important parts of the form are the empty spaces where you're asked to explain why you're the best person for the job. This is your opportunity to do your advertising!

— make it clear that you have read the job description thoroughly and if you have been to talk to someone already doing the job, or to other people in the organisation, refer to your conversations

— don't be afraid to leave some sections blank, eg: marital status. Make the rest really compelling and get the interview!

— translate your organisation or professional jargon so that the reader can relate to what you're saying

— explain the implications of the aspects of your past work

Get your results across

Practise describing your last two jobs in terms of results. Don't be modest. Blow your own trumpet!

JOB TITLE	RESULTS
Supervisor	Trained two juniors and a trainee in one year
	Reduced absenteeism by 20%
	Exceeded monthly targets

Curriculum vitae

Organisations often ask you to apply by sending your Curriculum Vitae. This is your opportunity to write your own sales material. Your CV is, literally, the story of your life, so it's up to you what you say and how you tell the story.

There is also no such thing as a standard CV – you will probably need to rewrite it and pitch it differently for every application. In addition, you may have a basic C.V. for networking which you feel represents you generally.

Nuts & Bolts

Do the same as for application forms, plus:

— three pages of A4 paper is the maximum length

— use good quality paper – consider the risk of using coloured paper to make it stand out

— name and number each page in a consistent way

— make sure it's well laid out and easy to read

— show your first draft to someone who will give you constructive feedback

— be prepared to rewrite it several times, if necessary

Content

— start with your name, address, work and home telephone numbers.

— education with dates and qualifications, from secondary school onwards. This can go after your career history if it's not your strong point.

— employment – start with your most recent work, as it's likely to be the one of most interest to the reader, and then go backwards, chronologically.

— describe career breaks as you would a period of paid employment. Refer to them as, for example; 'managing a home' and describe what you did; 'organised finances, managed changing priorities,' etc.

— the different bits of experience that you've had are increasingly described nowadays as your 'portfolio'. This may be something that you consciously work on extending, or a pattern that you identify with the benefit of hindsight.

— for each job, give the job title and department or company. Outline your responsibilities in one sentence for the most recent jobs. Follow this with a list of 3–6 notable achievements to prove how good you were. Jobs more than fifteen years ago simply need the job title, organisation and dates.

— other information you can include, but only if it helps your case, includes: date of birth, marital status, other awards, interests, referees, a photograph.

— include achievements outside paid employment which strengthen your case.

— conclude with items to list under 'interests'. Select them carefully, and make them interesting and different.

> ## Your personal resource bank
>
> Turn to Section 14 now and enter the key details you'll need to write any CV. It will help to prevent missing the deadline for an application while you find the key data.

> If you have an old CV, compare it with someone else's and consider what you could have done better.

Covering letters

CV's and application forms do not, strictly speaking, need covering letters, as they more or less speak for themselves. However, we suggest you use every opportunity to promote yourself and make yourself different, so always send a short covering letter:

— a maximum of one side of A4 paper

— use good quality paper and get it well typed

— make sure your name and address are clearly visible

— tell them what you're applying for, so you get considered for the right thing! Personnel departments are dealing with many applications for different jobs, course places, etc. at a time

— refer them to the best bits of your CV or application form

— condense your sales pitch into one short paragraph and tell them what's best or special about you

— EXPRESS ENTHUSIASM – it's a rare ingredient!

Interviews

All your work in this Workbook will be excellent preparation for job interviews. Revise any sections you consider will be important in applying for a particular job, check your personal resource bank and in particular take any action you need to on your image:

— refer back to the job description or advertisement. Use your skills audit on page 72 to see how you fit

— do not be put off if you don't fit all the criteria. Job adverts are written for the perfect person. When it gets to the interview, they're looking for the best person from the ones who've applied

— consider the interviewers' needs – what are they looking for? Revise your exercise on the customer on page 201

— what will have been sparked off in their minds by reading your application form? eg: if you've put down some very impressive achievements, they may want to know how you went about them, or what you enjoyed most about them

— how could what you say be misinterpreted? For example, if you overdo your enthusiasm to learn new things, it could be interpreted that you may not pay attention to the run-of-the-mill aspects of the job

— an interview is a 2-way process – be prepared to ask questions you could not have found answers to by your own research. Do not ask questions about things you should have discovered for yourself. Take a notebook into the interview and don't be afraid to refer to it or take notes of what you are told

— prepare to blow your own trumpet – that's what interviews are about. People often feel foolish doing this, especially if the people on the interview panel already know them. However, just because Eileen knows you day-to-day, it doesn't mean that she knows your aspirations, or how your current experience can be tailored to the new job. The interviewer(s) may also be observing how you deal with the stress of an interview, so don't hold back

About the practical arrangements

— if possible, discover where you come in the order of the day. If you are the tenth person they've interviewed that day, you'll need to pep up your performance to make yourself memorable. Equally so if you're the first – they'll still be settling down, and will 'warm up' on you

— find out how long you've got, so you can keep an eye on the time and ensure that you've said all your main points before time runs out

— plan your journey – aim to catch the earlier train or bus to get you there on time in case there are delays or allow puncture time if you're driving

— don't be afraid of telephoning them to ask for a map of how to get there, or of how to find them from the station – it shows that you've thought ahead, and are organised

About you

— think about your appearance – refer back to Section 11. You need to look comfortable and you need to look as though you fit the job/role you're applying for. Wear something that you feel good in and associate with success

— deal with nerves – the butterflies don't go away, but you can get them to fly in formation! Nerves help give you an edge – and sharpen you up. Go back to Section 10 to find hints and tips on getting your nerves under control

— get to know your nerves and the effect they have on you. You can then develop strategies to accommodate them, such as:

    — if your mind goes blank, have the main points you want to make noted down

    — if you get an upset stomach, get there early enough to discover where the 'Ladies' is, and give yourself a chance to get more comfortable

    — if you get a blotchy red neck, wear a high-necked shirt or sweater

    — try the breathing exercise on page 187

What you'll be asked

There's no set formula or list of guaranteed questions. Think about questions you may be asked specifically about your ability to do the job, questions that are topical, and questions that expand on the messages you've put on your application form or CV.

Don't take the questions at face value – think about what's behind the question.

Take your time before answering – don't be afraid of a pause. Much better to have a moment of silence than have you waffling on until you've realised what you want to say!

If you're applying for a management post, be ready to complete a psychometric assessment before the interview – possibly on the same day. These are used increasingly and are there to reveal your strengths and good qualities for the job, and are not there to catch you out or snoop on you. Don't be intimidated by it – grab the opportunity, complete the test openly and honestly and welcome the valuable feedback you'll get from it.

Practise

Practise with a friend, colleague or another woman working through this book. Practise an interview through. It helps your nerves to say some of the 'blow your own trumpet' things out loud before the big day, so that you feel more comfortable with them.

Keep applying for jobs, to raise your exposure and build up your experience of interviews.

Compare notes with friends and colleagues to discover which topical questions are asked at the moment.

> Keep a note of things you want to remember:

Remember:
— you have power in these situations – you can influence how your message is received in the way you put it across

— you are not being assessed on your value as a human being, you are being assessed for your suitability for a specific job/secondment/project/course

— they won't know how good you are unless YOU tell them!

Afterwards:

Whether you get the job or not, always ask for feedback on your application, interview performance and, if applicable, your psychometric assessment. Most interviewers are happy to do this over the phone and have been known to offer people alternative jobs!

It may be that you did really well, but simply weren't the appropriate person for this job. Asking for feedback:

— allays fears

— makes you memorable

— shows them that you take your aspirations seriously

— reminds them of your enthusiasm

— nearly always makes you feel better!

— helps you know yourself better

Other formal conversations

Other formal conversations are when you talk to your manager or another key person, in a situation such as an appraisal interview, a target-setting session, a performance review, staff-assessment interview or career development interview. (You can probably think of others specific to your organisation). Alternatively, you may find yourself in more casual conversations in the staff dining room or in a corridor, where it's just as important to create a good impression.

Use all these situations to put into practice all the points about blowing your own trumpet, and remember:

— you are building your image all the time

— all conversations contribute to the picture you're building of yourself

— grab opportunities to talk about your aspirations and achievements

— ensure your message is positive

Use phrases such as 'I've outgrown my job' rather than 'I'm bored' or 'I'm looking for something new' rather than 'It's the same old stuff' when someone asks how your work is.

Here are three questions people often ask, so make some notes here for your positive replies: –

'How are you getting on?'

> 'What are you doing these days?'

> 'What are you going to do next?'

Annual appraisal or performance-review interviews are a classic. How will they remember your particular achievements of almost a year ago, unless you remind them? It isn't being big-headed, it's being positive and self-confident.

These interviews and conversations are two-way processes, so do your preparation and go in there armed with your list of positive things to raise:

eg: — ask for feedback on your eligibility for another job

    — ask for training

    — ask for support for a secondment

    — list your achievements

> **Make a note here of things you want to raise:**

After all, you've got nothing to lose – **so have a go!**

Summary and action

By writing application forms and CV's in positive, results-orientated ways you'll increase your chances of success.

By making your general conversation about yourself positive and enthusiastic you'll enhance your image on a day-to-day basis.

Your personal resource bank

Make sure you've entered all the information you'll need next time you prepare an application form or CV.

Make a note on page 257 of your progress with interviews.

Further optional reading

Richard Bolles – *What Colour is your Parachute? – A Job Hunter's Manual* – published by 10 Speed Press

Action

What are you going to do now to make sure you blow your own trumpet?

Here are some suggestions:

— get feedback from a friend or colleague on your last or next application form
— look at jobs in the newspapers and consider how you could transfer your skills to do those jobs – if you wanted to
— discuss with your boss what you want to achieve in your present job

---

I will _____ by _____

I will _____ by _____

I will _____ by _____

I will _____ by _____

Profile

Mary E Blance
Senior Producer/Presenter – BBC Radio Scotland

I joined the BBC at Radio Shetland in 1978 as a secretary, the first to work full time since the station opened in May 1977. I was secretary from 1978-1981, Station Assistant 1981-1985, Producer 1985-1988, and since then I have been Senior Producer.

When I joined in 1978 I promised myself that if it was a dead end I'd move on in a year. I set about acquiring all the skills required in a community station. I was always willing to interview people when no-one else had the time; I'd do anything to get experience. But when I started work I felt like a square peg that had really found a square hole. I absorbed everything with enthusiasm. I retain that enthusiasm for my 'craft'.

I took every chance to learn the practical skills that are needed in a radio station – like editing, operating recording machines etc. I didn't have to learn any of this so I just did it at my own pace. As a result, I was able to become station assistant. During that period, I took many opportunities to compile complete programmes, work on the news, and do production work so that again I was ready to take on the job of producer when it became vacant.

Learning points: Be in the right place at the right time and always be ready to take the next step.

Don't wait around waiting to be offered opportunities to do things, volunteer. Look for areas where colleagues are under pressure and offer to lighten the burden.

Learn to use a tape recorder, practise writing news copy; whatever skill is relevant, learn it.

Don't neglect the work you are doing while your eyes are on other goals.

Never be seen with your bum on a radiator!

The woman who was Producer when I joined the station believed that in such a small unit (four people), everyone had to have all the skills. She encouraged me and gave me opportunities to use my own interests in local history, music, dialect etc., to make a variety of programmes. She was a very positive influence. There have been others who haven't been so encouraging, but I've got something positive from my experience with them too – learning how not to be like them in a working situation. So the potentially negative becomes positive. I am now very aware of my own possible role as 'mentor'.

My mother was a strong influence too. She was widowed young and left to bring up two daughters. She always trusted us to do the best we could in any situation. She never blamed us for any failure or misadventure, since she knew we'd have done our best. I also had an English teacher who taught me to love the spoken word and the sound of language. I'm privileged to have him among the team of local broadcasters I work with today.

My partner is very supportive, and rather good at persuading me to tackle things I don't want to do even when I know they're worthwhile.

Learning point: People matter – they give courage and good examples to copy or avoid.

Initially, I set myself the goal that if I didn't enjoy the work, and didn't get the chance to do anything apart from secretarial work, I'd leave in a year. I wanted to become involved in programmes, both news and feature programmes. From planning and doing short interviews, I built up to full-length programmes. All my targets were very programme-based, and I never saw myself in my present position, which is very much station figurehead in the community, with the PR work that it involves. Nor did I see myself as making decisions for the station, rather than as a programme maker. But here I am. I convinced myself it was a good idea to try for it since it was the next logical step. It's more fun than I thought it would be, and apart from a few ups and downs, including a 'blip' when I applied to become a salmon farmer, I still enjoy it.

Learning point: Identify your goals, and things you think you could do ... assess your positive points and know your limitations.

I'm not sure about my attitude to failure. I failed in teaching and just didn't enjoy the job at all, getting out of it as fast as I could. But I feel if you just can't do something well, it isn't a personal fault ... we all have different talents, and I can't take it personally if I'm not good at something particular. I'm not a great singer and will never get a place in a choir. I love singing and I've failed in any aspirations to go anywhere along that line, but I can still enjoy listening.

Learning point: Take a calculated risk – there's always a chance of failure.

The balance between work and home has swung this way and that, depending on the demands. I did have one boyfriend who resented the amount of time I had to spend at work. I now have a very supportive partner, whose own interests take up a lot of his time. I never take work home and stick rigidly to that rule. Most of all I value the time with my family and friends.

I feel my life outside the BBC is more important than the Corporation, which is only a part, though a very important part of my life. I'm still ME, Mary Blance, rather than Mary from Radio Shetland.

Learning point: Find the balance of work/home life that suits you. Take your holidays. When you're tired your work will be affected, and you might not know ... but other people will notice.

Having a hysterectomy in 1993 changed my quality of life dramatically, and some of my attitudes as well. It was a very tough decision to make, and it's only as my energy comes surging back months later, and I start to feel like a new person, that I realise it was the right thing to do. Throughout the whole frightening experience, (and things did take a wrong turn in the hospital), my husband and sister were with me ... though I felt guilty that they were losing holidays to be there. Since then, it's been sharing my own experience with other women who've been in the same position, that's kept my spirits up in the return to health. A friend and I continue to meet weekly, running our own support group for story-swapping.

Learning point: Don't feel guilty because you need to rely on other people; sharing experiences with other women can strengthen you.

YOU'RE STILL A WOMAN WITHOUT A WOMB.

MAKING IT HAPPEN

13

Life is to be lived. If you have to support yourself, you had bloody well better find some way that is going to be interesting. And you don't do that by sitting around wondering about yourself. What the hell – you might be right, you might be wrong – but don't just <u>avoid</u>.

Katherine Hepburn

Objective: To give you the support and encouragement to keep going

This section is important because:

— you're approaching the end of this Workbook
— this is the beginning of the rest of your life!
— you make things happen for yourself
— it's your life – to be lived!

Contents:

— dealing with failure
— building on success
— your energy and enthusiasm
— networking
— Springboard summary
— you have a choice
— action

Making it happen

— you've worked your way through 230 pages
— you've done lots of exercises – on your own and with others
— you've been asked all sorts of questions
— you've had to jot down your thoughts on every subject under the sun!

What does it all add up to?

— a load of rubbish?

— a lot of common sense?

— confirmation of what you already knew?

— a real eye-opener?

Whatever you think of this book, and wherever you are in your life, one thing is guaranteed:

NONE OF THIS WILL MAKE ANYTHING HAPPEN IN YOUR LIFE UNLESS YOU REALLY WANT IT TO

If you stretch yourself, you run the risk of failing, so consider your attitude to failure, and what your strategy will be for dealing with it.

Dealing with failure

Failure is a vital ingredient in your success.

If you continue to take your own development seriously, start behaving differently, set your goals and change things in your life, at some point or other you will fail. You have probably done so in your life already.

Failures and mistakes are normal and can be extremely helpful. Unless you're Superwoman, when you try out new things some failure is inevitable. It's how you deal with the failure that determines how positive or negative the experience turns out to be.

Numerous studies have been made of successful people in a wide range of occupations and at different levels in society. Some of these studies have tried to discover the common denominator that guarantees success: Factor X!

What these studies reveal is that successful people come from different backgrounds, have different conditioning, different motivations, live different lives and believe different things. But they all have Factor X – it's the nearest thing to a magic formula.

Factor X is: dealing with failure and having determination

Failure:

— stretches you
— sensitises you
— shows people you aren't afraid of taking risks
— can move you forward or move you back
— may teach you what you may need to do next
— challenges you and makes you stronger
— teaches you about timing
— gives you practice
— is painful!

In positive people, failure can bring out greater determination and the two together form a winning combination.

Learning from failure

Think back to what you regard as failures or mistakes in your life and with the benefit of hindsight, consider what they taught you. Many people say that what appeared to be a setback at the time often turns out to be a positive turning point in their lives:

Occasion	What you learnt
That terrible row with my manager	*Get my facts straight first*

'Charles Rennie Mackintosh said: "There is hope in honest error; none in the icy perfections of the mere stylist". If you aren't making mistakes, you aren't trying hard enough.'

Vikki Worthington
Researcher, Central Independent Television plc

Devise your own strategies for dealing with failure positively. Here are some that work for other people:

— gain feedback from your supporters

— talk to your mentor

— do things that you know you do well

— do little things to keep you moving

— review your achievements

— regain your inspiration

— read about other people's lives – all of them have overcome failures

— look for the miracles in every day. Miracles are the small, unlooked-for and unworked-for bonuses. Anything from a spectacular sunset to an unexpected act of kindness

How have you dealt with failure in the past?

Do you want to change this strategy? If so, what are you going to do differently?

Another part of dealing with failure positively is to be ingenious in the way you overcome the blocks that you meet. First of all:

Check you're using the system well

— find a secondment to provide the experience or skills that you need

— find out about grants, trusts, and scholarships which would get you new experience and new contacts, and where others would support you

— be alert to new projects and initiatives which could get you moving again

— consider moving sideways to enable you to come back at a higher level. Use your transferable skills to do this

— extend your contacts and ask their advice

Be ingenious about what you need

— consider a move to a smaller unit or department to become a bigger fish in a little pool and get more experience

— risk leaving and coming back. A lot of senior women put their success down to having done this

— arrange informally to shadow someone whose job you want to find out about – it need only be for a day

— volunteer and make yourself useful so you can learn what you need

— learn and practise skills outside work that you need for work

— use what you learn for work in your personal life where appropriate

— take on organising something special, such as a charity event, to get experience of managing other people and to raise your profile

— find a third choice where you're in an A or B situation. Not just a compromise but a real choice to break through

— turn problems into opportunities

Examples: Rafia was never considered for promotion because she'd become indispensable where she was. Once she realised this, she made a point of developing one of her team members to be just as capable as she was, and freed herself to be promoted.

Doreen qualified in accountancy in her late 30's, when on her career break. When she tried to return to work, she failed to get a job in accountancy because, while she had the qualifications, she had no experience. She overcame this by becoming the treasurer of the local Oxfam group who ran a spectacularly successful sponsored run. In her next application, Doreen was able to show how she had handled thousands of pounds in the last year. She got the job!

Building on success

Success:

— boosts your confidence

— tells you you've got it right

— shows people what you can do

— gives you energy

— happens every day

— encourages you

— speeds you up

— needs to be recognised – by you and others

— can make you complacent

— can spur you on to do more even when it will be more difficult

Everyone has their own personal definition of Success. Refer to yours on page 254.

Celebrate your success

Don't skip this part because generally you don't celebrate! In that case there's all the more reason to consider it.

Celebrating is a very good way to show that you value yourself.

Celebrating:

— is fun

— gives energy

— shows self-esteem

— is a reward

— establishes a milestone in your progress

You've almost finished this book. You've managed to find time in amongst everything else in your life to do the exercises – Congratulations!

What are you going to do to celebrate your achievements?

Your energy and enthusiasm

Along with failure, determination is the other hallmark of the successful person, so consider for a moment how you're going to make the most of your energy and enthusiasm to keep going.

Find activities to revive you:

The things that energise you will be very personal. Here are some ideas that other women have mentioned. Are yours here?

long walks	long bath
exercise class	a massage
an evening of TV	chat with a friend
day in bed alone	some domestic chores
day in bed with company	a swim
sunshine	sports
playing with the kids	being alone

Now add yours:

Which activities are your favourites?

Do you have a balance of activities between those:

— you do on your own and those you do with others?

— that cost nothing, very little or a lot?

— that take a long time or 5 minutes?

When did you last do these activities?

DO A REVIVING ACTIVITY DAILY – DO ONE NOW!

Networking

Throughout this Workbook we've encouraged you to renew old contacts and make new ones. If you've been working through the book in a group, then we hope that you've been giving each other ideas and support all the way through. If you've been working through the book on your own or with a friend, then we hope that you've been consciously extending your network to a wider range of people. Women network in a different way to the 'old boy network.'

To network well you'll:

— support each other and boost confidence

— share problems and information

— think in a networking way so if you can't help someone, you'll think of who you know who can

— make sure you don't pull the ladder up on those coming up behind

— be objective, straightforward and tactful in your feedback to each other

— celebrate each other's successes and support each other in your failures

— still compete for the same jobs

— laugh and sometimes cry together

— strengthen each other by mutual support

The value of networking is summed up in this little verse, *Support Systems*:

My right hand is being held
by someone who knows more than I,
and I am learning.
My left hand is being held
by someone who knows less than I,
and I am teaching.
Both my hands need thus to be held
for me – to be.

Natasha Josefowitz, *Is This Where I Was Going?*

Setting up a network

If two or three of you agree to meet up for lunch to give each other ideas and support – that's a network! If you want to network more widely, tap into the Springboard network through the Springboard Newsletter. Equally, many groups of women have formed networks to network more formally and publicly:

— inside their organisation

— in their local area

— with people with similar ideas and aims

Many of these networks are well established, such as the Women's Institute, while some are smaller and more specific, such as 'Women in Fund-Raising'.

If you want to set up one of these more organised formal networks, use this checklist to get you started:

1 What is your objective?

To give support, lobby, offer training, be consultative, have fun, campaign, etc? Write it down and keep it clear and brief.

2 Who will be eligible to attend?

This needs to tie in specifically to your objective. Don't be afraid to keep the eligibility very tightly defined. There is a temptation to try to be all things to all women. Are you going to include men?

3 When are you going to meet?

Take it a step at a time and don't be afraid to change the frequency or time to fit in with the current needs.

4 Talk to your organisation

At the very least, inform them what you're doing. At the best, persuade them to support you, give you a room to meet in, etc. It is extremely important to have a good relationship and two-way communication with the organisation – usually through someone in Personnel.

5 What is the role of men?

As members, allies, speakers etc? Refer back to your objectives.

6 Where are you going to meet?

A room at work, local pub, hired conference room, someone's sitting-room etc? Refer back to your objectives.

7 What publicity do you need?

If it's an informal support network between a group of women who, say, met on a course, you won't need any publicity, but if your objective is to act as, say, a forum for training, you may need to think of posters, circulars, notices on computers etc.

8 What about the Trade Unions?

Talk to the relevant trade unions in your workplace before you start. They may have a women's group already, and so you need to be clear about how your network differs. Alternatively, networks can be misunderstood and called 'Women's Unions' especially if you speak up about issues such as workplace nurseries, or pension rights. Trade unions can see you as a threat, so build a good relationship.

9 Name?

Whatever reflects your objectives and members. Most groups are called simply 'Women in BP', 'Women in ICL', 'Women in British Rail', etc. However, one network was called 'The Monday Moot', because they specifically wanted to include men in their meetings too, and they met on Mondays!

10 Start small and let it grow

If there are three of you, you've started a network!

11 Who's going to organise it?

Networks that rely on one person only last as long as that one person can stand it – which is usually not long! Make sure responsibility and work is spread, and consider rotating responsibilities; Rank Xerox's network have rotating roles of chair and secretary for each meeting, to give each other practice in dealing with meetings.

12 Respond to the needs of the group

Be flexible and ingenious in your activities in responding to the needs of the group. There is no set way of running a network, so do whatever works for you.

13 Network with other networks

You can learn a lot from linking with other women's networks in your profession, area, industry, etc. Give each other ideas, training opportunities and most importantly – support. See the Appendix for names of some of the big national networks who may have branches local to you.

14 Start now!

> What are you going to do to extend and maintain your networks?

For example: Following a training course, a group of women in BBC Scotland continued to meet informally to give each other support. Encouraged by their discussions, they have raised women's career development issues with the Personnel Department, resulting in further training initiatives. The original group has grown and also supports and links up with other groups in BBC Scotland who have spontaneously formed, following their lead.

Springboard Summary

The 15 sections of this book give you a self-development process that you can use over and over again, either on an ongoing basis, or when you are wanting to review and make changes. Go back and do any of the exercises, or work through any of the sections again whenever you want to.

Your Personal Resource Bank (section 14) is there for you to refer to whenever you need to. Keep it up to date and it will provide you with a compact and rich source of data to help you to:

— make a decision

— reassess yourself

— write an application form/CV

— go for an interview

— boost your confidence

— keep on track

In this Workbook you have:

— prepared yourself

— assessed the environment you're in

— assessed yourself

— assessed the support from other people

— set your goals

Once your goals were set, you have:

— gained the information you need

— gained assertiveness skills to help you

— looked at your image and the signals you send out about yourself

— developed healthy stress strategies

— dealt with failure and success

— built your networks

How are you getting on?

If you've been working through the Workbook in great detail then you have done a lot of work and covered some very difficult issues.

If you've been working in a group then maybe you've done some bits, and skipped over others to keep up with your group.

If you've been reading the book without doing the exercises, we'd like to encourage you to go back and try doing some of the work, because what looks simple or obvious in writing can be quite difficult in practice.

Review your own progress here:

Did you achieve the objectives you set yourself on page 13:

— in full?

— in part?

Where did you have difficulty?

How did you overcome the difficulty?

What went really well and why?

Where did your support come from?

How far have you achieved the goals you set in Section 6?

What have you learnt that you will take into the future?

In which ways do you feel differently about yourself and your situation?

You have a choice

As you know, there is nothing magic in this Workbook. All the strategies and techniques are common sense, born out of the experiences of the hundreds of women we've met on courses and in our travels.

Doing all the things we've suggested in this Workbook is not enough. You have to WANT to do it, and to continue to want to do it, so:

You have a choice – every day.

Every day you can decide whether to make the effort, take the risk, and take another step in your own journey. Every day you can decide not to – you can lose your energy and let it go. If you falter, you can pick yourself up again, dust yourself off and have another go – it's up to you.

You have total freedom in your choice

No one is going to make it happen for you, you have to make it happen for yourself, and every day you can renew your commitment freely – or not.

What you do, and how you do it are entirely up to you. We would simply say – DO IT! We believe it's important that you do, because that way you will become more fully yourself.

Live the life that you choose for yourself – not the life that your parents mapped out for you, or that your partner assumes for you, or that you seem to have fallen into. Make the choice, and then put it into action, through small practical steps, or big dramatic leaps – whatever fits you best.

Whatever it is that you decide to do – we wish you your own definition of success in doing it!

Our deepest fear is not that we are inadequate
Our deepest fear is that we are powerful beyond measure
It is our light, not our darkness, that most frightens us
We ask ourselves, 'Who am I to be brilliant, gorgeous, talented, fabulous?'
Actually, who are you not to be? You are a child of God.
Your playing small doesn't serve the world.
There is nothing enlightened about shrinking so that other people won't feel insecure around you.
We are all meant to shine, as children do.
We are born to make manifest the glory of God that is within us.
It is not in some of us; it is in everyone.
And as we make our own light shine, we unconsciously give others permission to do the same.
As we are liberated from our fear, our presence automatically liberates others.

Nelson Mandela

Action

What are you going to do now, to continue taking steps in your life?

I will _____ by _____

I will _____ by _____

I will _____ by _____

I will _____ by _____

I will _____ by _____

I will _____ by _____

A journey of 1,000 miles starts with a single step

YOUR PERSONAL RESOURCE BANK

14

Objective: To compile a reference book of useful information about yourself for future use

Your personal resource bank

This section gives you headings under which you build up your bank of useful data about yourself. It means that you keep all the overall facts and ideas about yourself in one place, and gives you material to refer to whenever you want to review or change anything in your life. It will be particularly useful to you when you:

— apply for a job

— prepare for an interview

— face a difficult life situation

— are faced with change

— want to reset goals

— write your CV

— make decisions

— want to revive your determination

At the end of each section in this Workbook there are suggestions on what to put in your personal resource bank. Also use it to record anything else you find useful.

Change

My usual responses to change at home and at work:

Aspects of change that I particularly enjoy:

Aspects of change that I find difficult:

Things that I get really angry or moved about:

My qualifications

School Qualifications
eg: CSE's, GCSE's, GCE's, Scottish Leaving Certificates:

Eng Art Soc Economic

Other Qualifications taken at School
eg: Duke of Edinburgh award, Queen's Guide, life-saving certificates, music
certificates

College, Art School or University Qualifications
eg: secretarial qualifications, RSA typing awards, degrees, post-graduate degrees,
City and Guilds, college diplomas, B.TEC, NVQ's, technical qualifications

Courses attended where no formal qualifications were given at the end

Professional Qualifications
Also include courses that you're part way through

Qualifications I need/want to get in the future

Anything else?

The positive advantages to me of:

Being a woman:

Being the age I am:

Lots of experience of career + life

Being the race/colour I am:

Having my level of physical ability:

Values

The things I value most highly are:

IN THE WORLD	AT WORK	IN RELATIONSHIPS	FOR MYSELF

Strengths and weaknesses

The qualities that are my strengths are:

The ones I'm working on keeping in balance are:

Achievements

The things I've achieved are:

At school/college:

Outside paid employment:

In my present work:

In my previous job(s):

Achievements

In relation to myself:

In relation to other people:

The achievement I'm particularly proud of is:

Other things I want to keep a note of:

Transferable skills

My best skills are:	An example of using them well is:

In addition, other people say I am also good at:

People

People who are actively helping me now are:

People who I am going to help to help me are:

Information I've found out about Networks:

Goals

My overall, long-term goals are:

My definition of success for me is:

Assertiveness

Situations at work where I know I can be assertive are:

Situations at home where I know I can be assertive are:

Situations where I know I can be assertive with myself are:

Blowing my own trumpet

Feature about me	Evidence of this	The benefit to others

Blowing my own trumpet

Things that make me special or different are:

When I go for interviews, I know I'm good at:

The aspect I need to work on is:

MY WORK HISTORY

Dates	Organisation/Department	Job Title	Achievements

MY WORK HISTORY

Dates	Organisation/Department	Job Title	Achievements

MY WORK HISTORY

Dates	Organisation/Department	Job Title	Achievements

MY WORK HISTORY

Dates	Organisation/Department	Job Title	Achievements

Other things I want to keep a note of:

APPENDICES

5

Appendix 1   **Useful addresses**
— The Authors
— Campaigning Groups
— Equal Opportunities
— Health and Well Being
— Lesbian Support
— Study
— Women's Networks
— Working Mothers and Families

Appendix 2   **Useful books and videos**
— Assertiveness
— Biographies
— Disability Issues
— Health
— Organisations
— Personal Development
— Race Issues
— Relationships
— Sexuality
— Skills
— Women's Issues
— Women and Work
— Videos

Appendix 1 – Useful Addresses and phone numbers

The address given in most cases, particularly for networks, is that of the Headquarters. Write to them to obtain the address of your local or regional branch. Many of the organisations are run voluntarily and would appreciate a stamped addressed envelope with your enquiry.

THE AUTHORS

Liz Willis and Jenny Daisley

The Springboard Consultancy
PO Box No 69
Stroud, Glos GL5 5EE
Tel: 01453 878540
Fax: 01453 872363

CAMPAIGNING GROUPS

Greater London Association of Disabled People

336 Brixton Road
London SW9 7AA
Tel: 0171 346 5800
Fax: 0171 346 5810
Minicom: 0171 346 5811
Provides masses of information for disabled people in London, and a newsletter for disabled women

Maternity Alliance

45 Beech Street
London EC2P 2LX
Tel: 0171 588 8583 (Office and minicom)
0171 588 8582 (Information)
Fax: 0171 588 8584
Working to make life better for pregnant women, new parents and their babies

New Ways to Work

309 Upper Street
London N1 2TY
Tel: 0171 226 4026
Job sharing and other flexible working arrangements. Information, publications, seminars and presentations

National Alliance of Women's Organisations (NAWO)

Suite 44, Diamond House
37-38 Hatton Gardens
London EC1N 8EB
Tel: 0171 242 0878
Umbrella organisation – support/ information/representation

National Council of Women

36 Danbury Street
London N1 8JU
Umbrella organisation – regional councils, information and lobbying

Women's Local Authority Network

The Pankhurst Centre
60-62 Nelson Street
Manchester M13 9WP
Tel: 0161 274 3684
Fax: 0161 273 6896

RADAR

12 City Forum, 250 City Road
London EC1V 8AF
Tel: 0171 250 3222
Up to date information on disability issues

Rights of Women

52-54 Featherstone Street
London EC1Y 8RT
Tel: 0171 251 6577
Free legal advice and assistance for women

The Fawcett Society

5th Floor, 45 Beech Street
London EC2Y 8AD
Tel: 0171 628 4441
Fax: 0171 628 2865

Campaigning for changes in legislation to give women true equality. Also gives information. Founded during the suffrage movement in 1866

The Suzy Lamplugh Trust

The National Charity for Personal Safety
14 East Sheen Avenue
London SW14 8AS
Tel: 0181 392 1839
To create a safer society and enable all people to live safer lives

The 300 Group

PO Box 353
Uxbridge UB10 0UN
Tel: 01895 812229
An all-party national organisation which aims to get 300 women MPs in the House of Commons; encourage women to seek and hold public office; encourage women to part- icipate in public decision making

Training 2000

16 Forth Street
Edinburgh EH1 3LH
Tel: 0131 550 3763
Fax: 0131 550 3762

Womankind

3 Albion Place
Galena Road
Hammersmith
London W6 0LT
Tel: 0181 363 8608
Enabling women in developing countries to take greater control over their own lives by funding practical projects

EQUAL OPPORTUNITIES

Commission for Racial Equality

Information Dept.
Eliot House
10-12 Allington Street
London SW1E 5EH
Tel: 0171 828 7022
Publishes a range of booklets and training materials

Equal Opportunities Commission

Overseas House, Quay Street
Manchester M3 3HN
Government organisation enforcing the Sex Discrimination Acts of 1975 and 1986 and the Equal Pay Act 1984 in Great Britain. Good source of information. Books and advice.

Equal Opportunities Commission

Stock Exchange House
7 Nelson Mandela Place
Glasgow G2 1QW
Tel: 0141 248 5833
The job of the EOC is to work towards the elimination of unlawful sex discrimination, to promote equality of opportunity between women and men. Also produces free/priced publications

Equal Opportunities Commission

Caerwys House, Windsor Lane
Cardiff CF1 1LB
Tel: 01222 343 552
Government organisation enforcing the equal opportunities legislation in Great Britain. Good source of information. Books and advice

Equal Opportunities Commission for Northern Ireland

Chamber of Commerce House
22 Great Victoria Street
Belfast BT2 7BA
Tel: 01232 242752
e-mail: info@eocni.org.uk
website: www.eocni.org.uk

Independent Public Body enforcing the equal opportunities legislation in Northern Ireland. Good source of information. Books and advice

The Wainwright Trust

1 Stortford Road, Standon,
Ware, Herts. SG11 1LT
Fund-raising to award study grants for individuals working in the field of equal opportunities in employment and dissemination of findings

TUC Equal Rights Department

Congress House
Great Russell Street
London WC1B 3LS
Tel: 0171 636 4030
Provides useful publications on Equal Rights and deals with a wide range of equality issues

Women's National Commission

Caxton House, Tothill Street
London SW1H 9NF
The official, independent, advisory body giving the views of women to the Government

HEALTH AND WELL BEING

Al-Anon Family Groups

61 Great Dover Street
London SE1 4YF
Tel: 0171 403 0888 (24-hour helpline)
Al-Anon offers understanding and support for families and friends of problem drinkers, whether the alcoholic is still drinking or not.
***Alateen**, a part of Al-Anon, is for young people 12-20 who have been affected by someone else's drinking, usually that of a parent. For details of meetings throughout the UK and Eire please contact the above*

Alcoholics Anonymous – General Office

PO Box 1, Stonebow House
Stonebow, York YO1 2NJ
Tel: 01904 644026
Voluntary, international fellowship of people wishing to stop drinking. Provides anonymity, group support and a 12-step programme for recovery. See telephone directory for your local group

Cruse-Bereavement Care

Cruse House
126 Sheen Road
Richmond
Surrey TW9 1UR
Tel: 0181 332 7227
Publications and national network and counselling for the bereaved

Eating Disorders Association

Sackville Place
44 Magdalen Street
Norwich NR3 1JU
Tel: 01603 621414
Helps sufferers and their families. Literature, support groups and telephone helpline

Elizabeth Garrett Anderson Hospital

Well Woman Centre
1st Floor, 144 Euston Road
London NW1 2AP
Tel: 0171 387 4598
Self-referral clinic staffed by women for women. Provides a range of screening services

Marie Stopes Clinic

Marie Stopes House
108 Whitfield Street
London W1P 6BE
Tel: 0171 388 0662
Advice on all women's health issues

National Association for Pre-menstrual Syndrome

PO Box 72, Sevenoaks
Kent TN13 3PS
Tel: 01732 741709

Write with SAE for membership details. Support groups and information

National Osteoporosis Society

PO Box 10, Radstock
Bath BA3 3YB
Tel: 01761 471771
Registered charity which provides help and support for sufferers of osteoporosis and campaigns for greater awareness in the general public, press and medical professions. Supports research

Rape Crisis Centre

Tel: 0171 837 1600 (24-hour helpline)

Release

Tel: 0171 729 9904
National agency offering advice, information and counselling for people using drugs – legal or illegal

Samaritan Hospital for Women

171 Marylebone Road
London NW1 5YE
Tel: 0171 402 4211

The British Slimnastics Association

Park House, 63 Park Street
Bridgend CF31 4AX
National network of classes by trained teachers. A 'whole person' approach to fitness

The Compassionate Friends

53 North Street
Bristol BS3 1EN
Tel: 0117 9539 639 (Help)
0117 9665 202 (Admin)
A nationwide self-help organisation of parents whose child of any age, including adult, has died from any cause. Personal and group support. Befriending, not counselling

The Dulwich Hospital – South Wing

East Dulwich Grove
London SE22 8PT
Tel: 0171 737 4000
Provides information on the menopause and osteoporosis

The Society of Teachers of the Alexander Technique

20 London House
266 Fulham Road
London SW10 9EL
Tel: 0171 351 0828
E-mail: stat@pavilion.co.uk
Website: http://www.pavilion.
co.uk.stat/welcome.html
For a list of qualified teachers and general information see page 186

Win Visible

Crossroads Women's Centre
PO Box 287
London NW6 5QU
Tel: 0171 482 2496
Produces information, leaflets and runs workshops. Promotes independence for women with disabilities

Women's Sports Foundation

305-315 Hithergreen, Lewisham
London SE13 6TJ
Tel/Fax: 0181 697 5370
A voluntary network of women committed to improving the opportunities for women in sport at all levels. Encourages women to keep fit and healthy

Women's Health

52 Featherstone Street
London EC1 8RT
Tel: 0171 251 6580
Helpline hours: 10am - 4pm
Mon, Weds, Thurs, Friday
Provides accessible information in a supportive manner to help women make their own informed decisions about their health

Women's Therapy Centre

6/9 Manor Gardens
London N7 6LA
Tel: 0171 263 6200
Founded in 1976 to provide psychotherapy for women with a feminist perspective. Also offers advice, information, training and publications

LESBIAN SUPPORT

Stonewall

16 Clerkenwell Close
London EC1R 0AA
Tel: 0171 336 8860
Campaign for civil rights for lesbians and gay men

Lesbian Line

Box 1514
London WC1N 3XX
Tel: 0171 251 6911
Minicom line: 0171 253 0924
Phone service for lesbians and advice on local numbers

Lesbian and Gay Switchboard:
Tel: 0171 837 7324

Gay's the Word

66 Marchmont St
London WC1N 1AB
Tel: 0171 278 7654
Mail order books – lesbian and gay reading

STUDY AND CAREERS

CRAC

Careers Research and Advisory Centre
Sheraton House, Castle Park
Cambridge CB3 0AX
Tel: 01223 460277
Enables individuals to build educational achievement and develop careers

The Federation of Image Consultants

3 George Foster Close
Earl Shilton
Leicester LE9 7RR
Tel: 01455 846700
Professional body to promote and provide standards for the image industry and personal development industry. Answers enquiries from members of the public about Image Consultants in their area

The Open University Business School

Walton Hall, Walton
Milton Keynes MK7 6AA
Tel: 01908 655888

The Open University

Walton Hall
Milton Keynes MK7 6AA
Tel: 01908 653449
For information on diploma and degree programmes and short courses. Special interest: 'Developing Women Managers'

Career Psychology

13 Harley Street
London W1N 1DA
Tel: 0171 637 2000

WOMEN'S NETWORKS

City Women's Network

Administrative Office
PO Box 353
Uxbridge UB10 0UN
Tel: 01895 275178
Network for professional women – mostly 'city' professions. Provides luncheons, training and acts as a voice for members' views

EWMD

International Amazone
10 Rue de Méridien
1210 Brussels, Belgium
Tel: 32 2 229 38 60
Fax: 32 2 229 38 01
E-mail:
100721.363@compuserve.com

European Women's Management Development Network. Very active multinational network for women managers. Annual conference and regular national meetings

London Women and Manual Trades

52-54 Featherstone Street
London EC1Y 8RT
Tel: 0171 251 9192
Fax: 0171 251 9193
Information on courses, videos, newsletter, list of tradeswomen, survey reports

National Federation of Women's Institutes

104 New Kings Road
London SW6 4LY
Tel: 0171 371 9300
Fax: 0171 736 3652

National Women's Register

3A Vulcan House
Vulcan Road North
Norwich NR6 6AQ
Tel: 01603 406767
Fax: 01603 407003
A national and international network of 10,000 women who meet locally to promote friendship and a 'better understanding of self and others'

Network

114B Cleveland Street
London W1P 5DN
Tel: 0171 222 2524
Network of senior women across all professions

Northwest Women into Management

1 Kew Drive
Davyhulme
Urmston
Manchester
M41 7UW
Tel: 0161 748 6081
Network for women in the north-west, interested in networking management/personal development

The RSA Women's Forum

8 John Adam Street
London WC2N 6EZ
Tel: 0171 930 5115
Royal Society for the encouragement of Arts, Manufacturers and Commerce. To encourage links with main women's organisations

Secretarial Development Network

13 Vicarage Close
Newbold Coleorton
Leics. LE67 8PG
Tel/Fax: 01530 223036
Promotes innovation in the development of the secretarial role

Single Again Network

Suite 33, 10 Barley Mow Passage
London W4 4PH
Tel: 0181 749 3745
National network after break-up or bereavement. Also publishes a magazine and provides an advice service

The Women's Environmental Network Trust

87 Worship Street
London EC2A 4BE
Tel: 0171 247 3327
Fax: 0171 247 4740
Gives advice and information about environmental problems which specifically affect women eg consumer goods, pollution and health transport, sanitary protection

Women in Banking and Finance

c/o Ann Leverett, Administrator
43 Keswick Road
West Wicham
Kent BR4 9AS
Tel: 0181 777 6902
Fax: 0181 777 7064
An independent bank sponsored networking group run by and for its members. Providing support and a varied calendar of events including training for women working in the financial sector

Women's Computer Centre

Wesley House, 3rd floor
4 Wild Court, Holborn
London WC2B 5AU
Tel: 0171 430 0112
Women-friendly courses and information on computers

Women's Engineering Society

Imperial College of Science & Technology
Dept of Civil Engineering
Imperial College Road
London SW7 2BU
Tel: 0171 594 6025
Professional body representing the interests of women engineers

Women in Management

5th floor, 45 Beech Street
London EC2Y 8AD
Tel: 0171 382 9978
Fax: 0171 382 9979
Network of women managers or those planning to be managers. Offers training and development activities and networking groups. Very active

Women in Publishing

c/o The Bookseller
12 Dyott Street
London WC1A 1DF
Network to provide forum for exchange and support and offer practical training for career and personal development

Women Returners Network

100 Park Village East
London NW1 3SR
Tel: 0171 380 0123
WRN aims to facilitate the re-entry of women to education, training and employment following a career break. It provides advice and information on training opportunities, free information sheets, a network, quarterly members' newsletter and an annual conference which addresses key themes concerning women's re-entry into the workforce

WORKING MOTHERS AND FAMILIES

Age Concern

Astral House,
1268 London Road
London SW16 4ER
Tel: 0181 679 8000
Fax: 0181 679 6069
Network of local Age Concern groups which offers a wide range of support and campaigning activities. Daycentres, support for carers. Information service. Self-help events. Check telephone directory for details of local groups

Carers National Association

20-25 Glasshouse Yard
London EC1A 4JS
Tel: 0171 490 8818

Charity to support those whose lives are restricted by caring for sick, disabled and elderly frail relatives and friends. Provides support, information and advice. Also lobbies government and other policy makers

Cry-sis

London WC1N 3XX
Tel: 0171 404 5011
Support group for parents of excessively crying and/or sleepless babies and young children. Also support for parents of children with behavioural problems eg tantrums, clingyness

Daycare Trust

Wesley House, 4 Wild Court
London WC2B 5AU
Tel: 0171 405 5617/8
Sister organisation to National Childcare Campaign. Provides a childcare information service to parents and others. Promotes affordable, accessible and equitable childcare services.

Family Mediators Association

The Old House,
Rectory Gardens, Henbury
Bristol BS10 7AQ
Tel: 0117 962 6300
Helps with family property and financial arrangements when parents/families split up

Gingerbread

16-17 Clerkenwell Close
London EC1R 0AA
Tel: 0171 336 8183
Promotes and supports local self-help groups for one-parent families. Also provides expert advice and information for lone parents

Hyperactive Children's Support Group

71 Whyke Lane
Chichester
West Sussex PO19 2LD
Tel/Fax: 01903 725182
Supports and advises parents/ professionals of hyperactive and ADHD children using dietary/ nutritional therapies. Literature available for sale

National Childbirth Trust

Alexandra House
Oldham Terrace, Acton
London W3 6NH
Tel: 0181 992 8637
The NCT offers information and support through pregnancy, birth and early parenthood. Over 400 branches nationwide offer antenatal classes, breastfeeding counselling and postnatal support

National Childcare Campaign Ltd

Wesley House, 4 Wild Court
London WC2B 5AU
Tel: 0171 405 5617/8
Campaigns for affordable, accessible, equitable and good quality childcare. Local membership, and also provides a national and local platform to promote childcare issues

National Childminding Association

8 Masons Hill, Bromley
Kent BR2 9EY
Tel: 0181 464 6164
Fax: 0181 290 6384
Membership organisation and charity which provides inform-ation, representation and support for registered childminders and parents. Promotes childminding as a quality childcare service. Provides low cost public liability insurance for registered childminders. Free information pack on receipt of SAE

Relate National Marriage Guidance Council

Herbert Gray College
Little Church Street
Rugby CV21 3AP
Tel: 01788 573241
Co-ordinates 126 local centres providing counselling for adults with relationship problems

Parents at Work

45 Beech Street
London EC2Y 8AD
Tel: 0171 628 3578
(information service)

Campaigns to improve the quality of life for working parents and their children. Provides advice to working parents and information to policy- and decision-makers. Works with employers to improve facilities and conditions for working parents and to acknowledge good practice. Provides informal support through a network of local groups

Women's Aid Federation of England

PO Box 391
Bristol BS99 7WS
Tel: 0117 944 4411 (Admin)
Tel: 0117 942 1396 (Training team)
Fax: 0117 924 1703
E-mail: wafe@wafe.co.uk
Tel: 0345 023 468 (National Helpline)
Helps women and children who are experiencing violence in the home

Parents Anonymous

Tel: 0171 263 8918
Helpline for parents in crisis

Widows Advisory Trust (National Association of Widows)

54-57 Allison Street
Digbeth
Birmingham B5 5TH
Tel: 0121 643 8348
Advice, information, friendship and support for widows

Working for Childcare

77 Holloway Road
London N7 8JZ
Tel: 0171 700 0281
Research and information to promote the development of quality childcare for working parents

Stillbirth and Neonatal Death Society

28 Portland Place
London W1N 4DE
Tel: 0171 436 5881
SANDS is run by bereaved parents for bereaved parents, to offer support when a baby has died at or around the time of birth. This includes support through subsequent pregnancies. SANDS offers one-to-one befriending: there are local group meetings.

Appendix 2 – Useful Books and Videos

This is not a definitive list but will get you off to a good start:

Assertiveness

Ken and Kate Back - *Assertiveness at Work* - MacGraw Hill - 1982
Considered by some to be the definitive book on assertiveness at work. Useful background reading.

Anne Dickson - *A Woman in your Own Right* - Quartet - 1992
Basic guide to assertion with emphasis on techniques - revised and updated.

Allan Pease - *Body Language* - Sheldon Press - 1981
Definitive guide.

Liz Willis and Jenny Daisley - *The Assertive Trainer* - McGraw Hill - 1994
A practical guide for trainers on their use of assertiveness.

Biographies

Anne Bancroft - *Weavers of Wisdom* - Arkana - 1989
Stories of women mystics of the twentieth century.

Sylvia Fraser - *My Father's House* - Virago 1989
Shows the courage of a woman finding healing for the pain of abuse.

Zerbanoo Gifford - *The Golden Thread* - Grafton Books - 1990
The personal experiences of Asian women who have made Britain their home.

Glenys Kinnock (ed) - *By Faith and Daring* - Virago Press - 1993
Interviews with 35 diverse and fascinating well known women. Great role models.

Barbara MacDonald - *Look me in the Eye* - Women's Press - 1984
An autobiographical account of one woman's experience of ageism.

Pearlie McNeill (ed) - *Through the Break* - Sheba Feminist Publishers - 1986
Personal experiences of women in crises and how they coped.

Disability Issues

AA - *Guide for the Disabled Traveller*
List of 300 British hotels suitable for disabled travellers. European touring information with lists of suitable accommodation.

Jo Campling - *Images of Ourselves* - Routlege, Kegan & Paul
A collection of short biographies by disabled women - all ages and kinds of disabilities

Darnborough and Kinvade - *Directory for the Disabled* - Radar
Handbook of information and opportunities for disabled people.

Anne Finger - *Past Due* - The Women's Press - 1991
A story of disability, pregnancy and birth.

Lois Keith (ed) - *Mustn't Grumble* - The Women's Press
Anthology of disabled women's writing.

Gwyneth Ferguson Matthews - *Voices from the Shadows* - The Women's Press - 1983
Disabled women speak out.

Jenny Morris - *Able Lives* - The Women's Press - 1990
Accounts from 200 women who have sustained spinal injury resulting in varying degrees of impairment or paralysis.

Jenny Morris (ed) - *Encounters with Strangers* - The Women's Press - 1996
Challenging and thought-provoking selection of essays strongly arguing the need for the feminist movement to embrace issues for disabled women.

Jenny Morris - *Pride against Prejudice* - The Women's Press - 1991
Transforming attitudes to disability.

Health

Jeanne Achterberg - *Woman as Healer* - 1990
The healing activities of women from prehistoric times to now.

Jacqueline Alkenson - *Coping with Stress at Work* - Thorsons - 1988
Good all round book.

Anne Dickson and Nikki Henriques - *Hysterectomy. The women's view* - Quartet - 1994
Demystifies the facts around hysterectomy and describes women's experiences.

Germaine Greer - *The Change* - Hamish Hamilton - 1991
Women, ageing and the menopause.

Louise Hay - *You can Heal your Life* - Eden Grove Publications - 1988
The powerful effect of positive thinking on your health and well-being.

Hen Co-op - *Growing Old Disgracefully* - Piatkus - 1993
New ideas for getting the most out of life.

Shere Hite - *Women as Revolutionary Agents of Change* - Bloomsbury - 1993
A distillation of Shere Hite's research over 20 years into women's most personal feelings and experiences.

Leslie Kenton - *Passage to Power* - Vermillion - 1996
Brilliant book on the natural ways of living through the menopause.

Gail Sheehy - *The Silent Passage* - Harper Collins - 1993
Friendly explanation of the effect of menopause on individual women and society in general.

Chris Stevens - *The Alexander Technique* - Optima - 1987
Light, easily readable introduction.

Organisations

Charles Handy - *Beyond Certainty* - Arrow Books - 1996
How work and organisations need to manage and enjoy continuous uncertainty.

The Hansard Society Commission - *Women at the Top: Progress after 5 years* - 1996
Lots of statistics and examples - an antidote to complacency.

Barbara Rogers - *Men Only* - Pandora - 1988
Analysis of the effect and function of the many men-only organisations.

Personal Development

Richard Bolles - *What Colour is your Parachute?* - 10 Speed Press - 1996
A practical manual for job hunters and career changers. Excellent. Crammed with inspiration, information and lots of practical exercises.

Petruska Clarkson - *The Achilles Syndrome* - Element - 1994
Identifies the secret fear of failure felt by many apparently successful people. Explains the reasons and how to resolve the feelings of never being good enough.

Kaye Cleave - *Once more with Feeling* - Oliver publishers - 1996
Written by a Springboard trainer - a light and easy way of looking at emotional management as a key to success.

Stephanie Dowrick - *The Intimacy and Solitude Self-Therapy Book* - The Women's Press - 1993
Practical handbook of personal development exercises.

Louise Hay - *The Power is within You* - Eden Grove - 1991
How to overcome the emotional barriers we place in our own paths and reprogramme our headtapes to be more positive.

Thomas Harris - *I'm OK - You're OK* - Pan -1970
The classic description of Transactional Analysis. Has links with Assertiveness.

Amy Harris & Thomas Harris - *Staying OK* - Pan - 1985
The popular sequel to *I'm OK - You're OK*.

Susan Jeffers - *Feel the Fear and Do It Anyway* - Arrow Books - 1991
A recommended classic - how to turn your fear and indecision into confidence and action.

Susan Jeffers - *End the Struggle and Dance with Life* - Hodder and Stoughton - 1996
How to build yourself up when the world gets you down - very uplifting.

Carol Osborn - *Enough is Enough* - New World Library - 1992
Part autobiography and part practical exercises, to explore the idea of 'downward mobility' - how to stop trying to do everything perfectly and do what you want to do.

Anne Wilson Schaef - *Meditations for Women who Do Too Much* - Harper Collins - 1990
For all of us who do too much - a thought for every day - warm and perceptive. Required reading for workaholics and careaholics!

Race Issues

Maya Angelou - *I Know Why the Caged Bird Sings* - Virago
Autobiographical account of a black woman growing up.

Angela Davis - *Women, Race and Class* - The Women's Press

Peter Fryer - *Staying Power* - Pluto Press
The history of black people in Britain.

Linda Villarosa (ed) - *Body and Soul* - Harper Perennial

Relationships

Judith Arcana - *Every Mother's Son* - The Women's Press - 1996
The role of mothers in the making of men

Robert Bly - *Iron John* - Element - 1990
The much discussed book about men, possibly pioneering a new interest in men's development.

John Cleese & Robin Skynner - *Families and How To Survive Them* - Methuen - 1983
Excellent - a guide to understanding relationships in families.

Gudrun Davy & Bons Voors - *Lifeways - Working with Family Questions* - Hawthorn Press - 1984
An anthology about the renewal of family life. Shows how the tension between personal fulfilment and family life can be resolved. Sections on illness, clothing, food and discipline.

Dosey & Cums - *Lesbian Couples* - Seal Press
Written by and for lesbian women about couple relationships.

Dee Dee Glass - *All My Fault* - Virago - 1995
Explains why women don't leave abusive men.

John Gray - *Men are from Mars, Women are from Venus* - Thorsons - 1993
A practical guide to relationships between men and women.

Sam Keen - *Fire in the Belly* - Piatkus - 1992
One of the wave of books helping to find a new identity for men in today's world.

McKenzie, Loval, Gray & Muir - *Taking Care of your Elderly Relatives* - Allen & Unwin
For those who look after elderly people.

Ann Moir & David Jessel - *Brain Sex* - Mandarin - 1989
The differences in the ways in which men and women's brains work.

Robin Norwood - *Women who love too much* - Arrow Books - 1986
For the woman who loves men who don't love back. Recommended.

M Scott Peck - *The Road Less Travelled* - Rider - 1987
New understandings about love, relationships and personal development.

Victoria Secunda - *When You and Your Mother can't Be Friends* - Heinemann - 1991
An eye-opener. Explains the difficulties in the mother/daughter relationship and offers practical advice to help heal and let go.

Victoria Secunda - *Women and their Fathers* - Cedar - 1993
The companion volume to her book on mothers.

Deborah Tannen - *You Just Don't Understand* - Virago - 1992
A real eye-opener. Identifies the different ways in which men and women use conversation and explains why there are so many misunderstandings in our communications.

Deborah Tannen - *Talking from 9-5* - Virago - 1994
Who gets heard and who gets credit for work done.

Sexuality

Anne Dickson - *The Mirror Within* - Quartet - 1985
A new look at sexuality for women.

Gloria Dussback - *Are you still my Mother/Are you still my Family?* - Warner Books - 1985
Coping with family reactions to lesbians 'coming out'.

Angela Mason and Anya Palmer - *Queer Bashing* - Stonewall - 1996
Survey report and personal stories of the violence and harassment experienced by lesbians and gay men in the UK - horrifying and sobering reading.

Christine McEwan & Sue O'Sullivan (eds) - *Out the Other Side* - Virago - 1988
Excellent starting book for women who think they may be lesbian or who may wish to 'come out'. Covers many issues for lesbian women.

Rich Rasi (ed) - *Coming Out in the Workplace, the Perils and Pleasures of Coming Out on the Job* - Alyson Publications - 1995

Skills

Jessica Davis - *Protect Yourself* - Piatkus - 1991
A handbook specifically for women with practical measures you can take to protect yourself, your property and your children.

Margaret Doyle - *The A-Z of non-sexist language* - The Women's Press - 1995
Very useful reference book and fascinating essays on the derivations of various words.

Michael Gelb - *Present Yourself* - Aurum Press - 1988
A simple guide to giving powerful presentations.

Diana Mather - *Image Works for Women* - Thorsons - 1996
A wide ranging look at making your image work for you.

Stephan Rechtschaffen - *Time Shifting* - Doubleday - 1996
Much more useful than a time-management book, explains how to change your relationship with time and start relishing and living life to the full.

Eleri Sampson - *The Image Factor* - Kogan Page - 1995
Dovetails beautifully with and refers to *Springboard* - a practical companion volume on all aspects of image.

Dale Spender - *Nattering on the Net* - Spinifex - 1995
Great book explaining how the Internet works and the importance of women getting involved.

Cristina Stuart - *Effective Speaking* - Pan - 1988
An essential guide to making the most of your communication skills.

Women's Issues

EOC - *Women and Men in Britain* - HMSO -1996
36-page booklet packed with the facts about how we live our lives.

Susan Faludi - *Backlash* - Chatto and Windus - 1991
The prize winning and controversial assessment of the effect of feminism. Much talked about.

Kate Figes - *Because of her Sex* - Macmillan - 1994
Shows how equality for women in the UK is given lip service but is not supported by current policies or practice.

Marilyn French - *The War Against Women* - Hamish Hamilton - 1992.
Packed with facts and objective research information. Disturbing assessment of the position of women in society.

Lesbian History Group - *Not a Passing Phase* - The Women's Press - 1989
Reclaiming lesbian history 1840-1985.

Sarah Nelson - *Incest - Fact and Myth* - Stramuttion Co-operative - 1987
Practical, factual and helpful guide for survivors.

Dale Spender - *Man Made Language* - Routledge and Kegan Paul - 1985
The definitive book on the way our language devalues women. Good awareness-raising stuff.

Dale Spender - *Women of Ideas (and what men have done to them)* - Ark Paperbooks - 1982
A history of women's thought and creativity.

United Nations - *The World's Women 1970-1990* - United Nations -1991
Fascinating and often disturbing trends and statistics.

Bernadette Vallely - *What Women Want* - Virago - 1996
A snapshot of what women in the UK want, in all aspects of their lives - good quotes.

Susan Alice Watkins and others - *Feminism for Beginners* - Icon Books -1994
Heavily illustrated and fun to read - a crash course in the history of the feminist movement.

Naomi Wolf - *Fire with Fire* - Chatto and Windus - 1993
Controversial voice of the 'new' woman, poses challenges.

Women's National Commission - *Directory of Women's Organisations*
Catalogues all the women's organisations in the UK. Free

Women and Work

Clare Brant & Yun Lee Too - *Rethinking Sexual Harassment* - Pluto Press - 1994
Selection of essays from a wide range of perspectives.

Sally Cline & Dale Spender - *Reflecting Men at Twice their Natural Size* - Fontana -1987
Why working women make men feel good.

Margaret Flanders - *Breakthrough* - PCP - 1994
Practical guide for career women on shattering the 'glass ceiling'.

Barbara Killinger - *Workaholics, The Respectable Addicts* - Simon and Schuster - 1992
By far the best and most helpful book on workaholism with practical strategies for recovery.

Scarlett McGwire - *Best Companies for Women* -Pandora Press - 1992

Bonnie C. McKenzie - *Friends in High Places* - Business and Professional Publishing - 1995
Written by a Springboard trainer. Lots of hints and tips on finding and making the most of a mentor.

Lily Segerman-Peck - *Networking and Mentoring (A Woman's Guide)* - Piatkus - 1991
Practical guide specifically for women to maximise the value of mentors and networks.

Liz Willis & Jenny Daisley - *Developing Women Through Training* - The Springboard Consultancy - 1997
A practical how-to-do-it guide on women's development training. Written for organisations and women's groups.

Women Returners Network - *Returning to Work* - Longman
Directory of Education and Training for women - regularly updated.

Videos

Through the Glass Ceiling - Leeds Animation Workshop
Excellent cartoon illustrating all the serious points about the blocks to women in employment in an easy-to-watch and listen-to way.

Patsy Rodenberg - *A Voice of Your Own* - Vanguard Productions
Practical exercises to bring out the best in your voice.

The Eye of the Storm and *A Class Divided* - Concord Video and Film Council
Documentaries on the startling work done on race awareness in a primary school in the USA.

Crosstalk - BBC Education
A look at cross-cultural communication.

Orders

If you have any difficulty ordering *Springboard* from a bookshop, you can order direct from Hawthorn Press, 1 Lansdown Lane, Stroud, GL5 1BJ, UK.

Tel: 01453 757040   Fax: 01453 751138

Other books from Hawthorn Press

Enterprise of the Future
Moral Intuition in Leadership and Organisational Development
Friedrich Glasl

Friedrich Glasl describes the future of the modern organisation as a unique challenge for personal development. Every organisation, whether a business, a school, a hospital or a voluntary organisation, will have to develop closer relationships with the key stakeholders in its environment – its suppliers, customers, investors and local communities. Our consciousness needs to expand beyond the boundaries of the organisation to work associatively with the community of enterprises with whom we 'share a destiny'.

216 x 138mm; 128pp; paperback; ISBN 1 869 890 79 5.

Raising a Son
Parents and the Making of a Healthy Man
Don Elium and Jeanne Elium

Many parents feel frustrated and confused by the behaviour of their sons and are in need of some practical guidance. *Raising a Son* offers just that: advice on firm but fair discipline that will encourage the awakening of your son's healthy soul.

A much needed and brilliant resource for fathers and mothers.
        Dr John Gray, author of *Men are from Mars, Women are from Venus*

215 x 138mm; 256pp; paperback; ISBN 1 869 890 76 0.

Tapestries
Weaving Life's Journey
Betty Staley

Tapestries gives a moving and wise guide to life phases. Drawing on original biographies of a wide variety of people, Betty Staley offers a vivid account of life journeys. This book helps readers reflect their own lives and prepare for the next step in weaving their own biographical tapestry.

216 x 138mm; paperback; ISBN 1 869 890 15 9.

Water, Electricity and Health
Protecting Yourself from Electrostress at Home and Work
Alan Hall

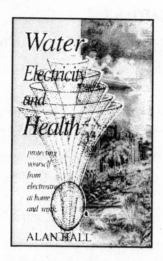

This book will help you understand how electrostress affects you. New light is cast on the secrets of water, life and electricity. You can then take steps to neutralise electrostress and increase your energy.

Electrostress is now pervasive. Symptoms can range from fatigue, tension, poor resilience to insomnia, low immunities and serious illness. Houses near pylons and transformers are hard to sell. But whilst scientists accept electrostress, nobody has yet discovered just how electromagnetic fields cause ill health.

When physicist Alan Hall found that underground streams linked a stricken home to nearby power cables, the family moved and recovered their health. He then asked how water transmits electrostress. Here, he invites you to accompany his fascinating journey of discovery into the nature of water as bearer of life, and as carrier of death. His major discovery of biodynamic fields is applied to countering the harmful effects of electromagnetic fields.

210 x 135mm; 192pp; paperback; ISBN 1 869 890 94 9.

Rivetting and informative; the first book I have seen that brings a holistic understanding of how electricity affects life – and what we can do about it.

Christopher Day –
ecological architect and
author of *Places of the Soul.*

Vision in Action
Working with Soul and Spirit in Small Organisations
Christopher Schaefer and Tyno Voors

Vision *facilitates the vital process of social innovation.*

Hazel Henderson

Thoroughly revised and updated second edition. This is a user friendly, hands on guide for developing small organisations such as companies, schools and charities.

216 x 138mm; 256pp; paperback; ISBN 1 869 890 88 4.

Workways
Seven Stars to steer by
Kees Locher and Jos van der Brug

Are you in a position to influence and help others to make career choices? Are you sure that you are steering them in the right direction? Help is at hand with *Workways, Seven Stars to Steer By,* developed over the last 20 years. It contains 37 exercises and tips for you to help people find their next step. It will help you assist others build their vision for their work, clarify direction, focus their energy, discover their sources of inspiration and lead to renewal. The background readings include the biography of Cezanne, illustrated in colour. The tasks, tips and creative activities are carefully geared to the needs of individuals and groups.

297 x 210mm; 352pp; paperback; ISBN 1 869 890 89 2.

Manhood
An action plan for changing men's lives
Steve Biddulph

Manhood is having a profound impact on the lives of men and women since publication in Australia. Well read copies are passed from hand-to-hand-by friends, partners, work mates, from sons to fathers – with the simple message, 'You must read this!'

This practical book is full of helpful insights, personal experiences and solutions. It is written for older men, young men, working men, unemployed men, business men, fathers and sons. It is also written for women who want to love and understand men's growth.

Manhood is unique because it tackles the key areas of a man's life – being a real father, love and relationships, masculinity, finding the heart in work, helping boys with school, making real friends and personal development. It opens new pathways to healing the past and forming true partnerships with women, whilst helping men respect their inner needs as individuals.

Steve Biddulph is a family psychologist. He was born in Yorkshire and lives in Tasmania. He makes regular lecture tours to Britain. His books *Raising Boys, The Secret of Happy Children* and *More Secrets of Happy Children* have sold half a million copies in five languages.

Readers on *Manhood*

From men:
Manhood has given me the first inkling in my life of what it is to be an integrated, self respecting man.

It finally gave me the courage to approach my father and mother, and sort things out...
I feel lighter, happier, freer, healthier, emotionally and physically.

Manhood is a wonderful book. It made me cry. It crystallised and explained so many things.

From women:
It would be true to say that *Manhood* has transformed how I see my husband and father. It moved me to tears many times. It has brought us closer than ever.

I felt it uncovered the deep longings all of us have for some kind of balance, meaning and purpose to our living and loving.

216 x 138mm; 272pp; paperback; 12 black and white photos; ISBN 1 869890 99 X

Orders: Advance or direct orders are welcome. Payment by credit card to Scottish Book Source, Tel: 0131 229 6800